THE
PRACTICAL
BOTANIST

THE
PRACTICAL BOTANIST

Michael Jordan

Facts On File
New York • Oxford

A QUARTO BOOK

For information contact:

Facts On File Limited
Collins Street
Oxford OX4 1XJ
United Kingdom

A British CIP catalogue record for this book is available from the British Library

ISBN 0-8160-2312-3

Facts On File books are available at special discounts when purchased in bulk quantities for businesses, associations, institutions or sales promotions. Please contact the Special Sales Department on 0865-728399.

Designed and produced by Quarto Publishing plc, The Old Brewery, 6 Blundell Street, London N7 9BH

Senior Editor: Sally MacEachern
Editor: Diana Brinton
Designer: Claire Finlaison
Art Editor: Anne Fisher
Artists: Kevin Maddison, Ann Savage
Photography: Michael Jordan, Betty Jordan,
Rob Cousins (equipment pp40-43)
Index: Sue Robertson

Assistant Art Director: Chloe Alexander
Art Director: Moira Clinch
Publishing Director: Janet Slingsby

Typeset by Ampersand Typesetting Ltd
Manufactured in Hong Kong by Regent Publishing Services Ltd
Printed by Leefung-Asco Printers Ltd, Hong Kong

10 9 8 7 6 5 4 3 2 1

CONTENTS

GETTING STARTED

MAKING THE RECORD

WOODLAND FLOWERS AND TREES

GETTING STARTED
INTRODUCTION

That "all flesh is grass" is an accurate maxim. Either directly or indirectly every member of the animal kingdom owes its health and well-being to the plant world. It is particularly apposite in the modern world, where attention is focused ever more sharply on the precarious state of the environment. Terms like "biosphere" and "greenhouse effect", which would have made little sense in our grandparents' day, reflect, as the millennium runs to its close, issues of extreme importance, and there can be little doubt that one of the keys to the future success or failure of our planet to sustain life in any shape or form lies with green plants. The natural regulation of vital gases in the earth's atmosphere depends to a large extent on the healthy metabolism, the day-to-day activities of a vast quantity of green life forms, ranging from delicate green slimes floating ephemerally on pond surfaces, to mighty and time-honoured forest trees.

European climates

For the well-being of a green plant, Europe – the continental land mass and the assortment of off-shore islands including the British Isles – represents something of both paradise and purgatory. Across Europe, the climatic zones within which certain plants can thrive vary from arctic, through temperate, and into sub-tropical. There exist long coastlines, salt marshes, lakes and rivers, meadows, forests, and infinite variations of soil type and altitude. Europe can, in other words, provide almost all the climates found on earth, short of those needed to sustain tropical rain forests or true desert flora, and this means that the overall total of plant species is potentially enormous.

Against this, virtually none of the European landscape is other than man-made or man-manipulated,

Below In spite of atmospheric pollutants, agricultural sprays, and chemicals leaching into the soil from effluent-laden waterways, the practical botanist who ventures into the European countryside, by car or on foot, will still discover a rich environment, for the European landscape supports at least 15,000 species of wild flowering plants.

and the number of habitats in which wild plants can establish and grow undisturbed has shrunk to a fraction of that which existed even a hundred years ago. The air, soil and water with which plants have to cope have also become infinitely less healthy, a deterioration attributable partly to incidental man-made pollution, and partly to deliberate application of chemicals to agricultural and forested land.

Nonetheless, Europe retains a botanical bonanza. The British Isles has almost 1,300 species of flowering plants, which sounds a large figure on its own, but which pales into insignificance when one discovers that across Europe the total rises to something over 15,000. This figure does not include the mosses, fungi, algae, and lichens, the numbers of which run into tens of thousands when one includes all the microscopic forms of plant life that colonize everything from a rain puddle to the tiles on the roof.

Top The great European forests were cut down in distant times, and the fields and hedgerows that replaced them are exclusively man-made.

Above Sadly, temperate wild-flower meadows are becoming a rarity, but they still exist and, once discovered, provide a seasonal delight rarely surpassed in nature.

7

IDENTIFYING PLANTS

Traditionally, there tends to be a separation between professional botany and amateur wild plant identification, yet the intricate world of greenery possesses fascinations which only reveal themselves properly if one steps beyond the mere tracking down of a specimen and ticking it off a list. Exploring the plant world in more depth does not have to be an intimidating venture that relies heavily on tongue-twisting jargon and scientific apparatus. With a few exceptions, most of the material requirements can be picked up in the high street on a small budget, and having mastered a few unfamiliar terms and processes the amateur is well on the way.

Perhaps the first thing with which it is essential to come to grips is the nomenclature – the way in which plants are classified and segregated into groups. Here, you are likely to find that you must abandon some of the common-or-garden notions: for example, your local florist may happily offer "grasses" for sale, but the practical botanist will separate these more correctly into grasses, rushes and sedges.

What are the characteristics which tell us that a plant belongs to one group rather than another? The lower echelons of ferns, mosses, liverworts and so on have their place later in the book, but as far as flowering plants – the Angiosperms – go, it is the crucial bits and pieces making up the flower that determine whether you are looking, for example, at a stinging nettle or a dead nettle (apart from the aggressive behaviour of one and the mild manner of the other). The number and arrangement of sepals, petals, stamens and pistil are the criteria on which the dead nettle falls into the *Labiatae* and the stinging nettle into the *Urticaceae*. Classification has not always been so accurate, and similar common names for plants which are biologically unrelated are often lingering reminders of groupings that are antiquated and much less rational.

Dicotyledones and Monocotyledones

The broadest classification of flowering plants is based, however, on the way the embryo is constructed. Take a look at a broad bean seed, or a lentil, or a peanut – when the coat is peeled off, the seed separates into halves. These fleshy lobes, or *cotyledons*, feed the embryo plant as it begins to grow, serving much the same purpose as the yolk in an egg.

The Dicotyledones develop two cotyledons, and are by far and away the largest group of the flowering

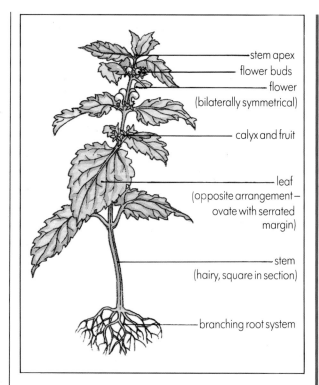

Above All flowering plants are distinguished into roots, stems, and leaves. The roots gather water and essential minerals and the stems support the leaves – the energy gathering organs – and the flowers.

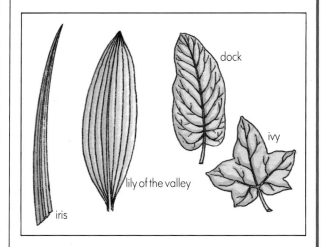

Above The leaves of Monocotyledones are distinguished by veins that run in parallel. Each plant is derived from a seed which contains a single food leaf or cotyledon.

Above The leaves of Dicotyledones have netted or reticulate veins, showing pinnate branching as in dock (*Rumex*), and palmate as in ivy (*Hedera*). Each seed has two cotyledons.

plants, with a range extending from anemones to ash trees and including such species as the broad bean. The Monocotyledones, to which belong the grasses, orchids, irises, and most plants that over-winter as bulbs and corms, produce only one. Other distinctions appear in the mature plant. Pick a leaf from a daffodil or an iris and notice how the veins run in parallel – this is typical of Monocotyledones. Another common feature is that their flowers usually have parts arranged in multiples of three. Compare your sample with a typical Dicotyledon, such as a broad bean plant or a dead nettle, and you will find that the leaf-veins of the latter tend to be branched into a net. Dicotyledon flower parts are arranged in fours and fives, and occasionally twos.

Roots, stems and leaves

Every flowering plant, regardless of classification, consists of three basic elements: a stem, which serves not only to support the leaves and flowers, but also as a plumbing and transport system; the roots, which anchor the stem in the ground and draw up water and minerals, and the leaves, which not only allow the plant to breathe but, equally importantly, are the principal food processing organs and part of the plant for which sunlight is indispensable.

There are many special modifications that break the general rules. Stems, for example, can form horizontal runners above ground, or suckers, or underground food storage organs like iris rhizomes, crocus corms and potato tubers, and even within the more typical constructions stems can be either simple or branched, upright or creeping, and are designated herbaceous or woody, according to the amount of strengthening material, lignin, that is laid down in their tissues. A dead nettle stem, designed to support a light weight of growth for just one season, builds very little lignin, while an oak trunk, needless to say, produces a great deal.

Leaves grow typically as flat plates because this construction allows them to present the maximum surface area, important both for their role as the plant's "lungs", and for absorbing the sun's rays. Here, too, special modifications arise to cope with particular living conditions, and the result may be anything from a leaf that has been reduced to a hard drought-resistant spike, to an inflated, rubbery, water-retaining cushion.

Roots, in the main, either branch through the soil in a random pattern, or develop as a single tap root with lateral rootlets. The tap root can become massively enlarged as a storage organ, like the carrot or parsnip, and sometimes aerial roots can develop above ground.

Pollination

The components of a flower are actually a modified shoot and leaves designed for one purpose: to effect pollination and fertilization. In other words, the flower is a seed factory, and since the pollination is engineered either by the agency of wind or by insects, the flowers are built accordingly. A flower designed for insect pollination relies on various features that will attract bees, butterflies and other insects. Hence, it develops large gaudy petals, sometimes incorporating parts of the colour spectrum that cannot be detected by the human eye. The insect-pollinated flowers also possess scent glands and nectaries, the honey-secreting organs. In a wind-pollinated flower, these welcoming features are reduced or missing, but in compensation the bloom is designed so that its pollen will catch the slightest breeze and will be able to land with reasonable certainty on the female parts of a neighbouring flower.

FLOWER TYPES

Just as one can distinguish between the simple life forms and the more advanced types in the animal kingdom, so too in the world of flowering plants the major groups are separated along an evolutionary ladder according to the sophistication of their flower structure. One of the most obvious distinctions between the construction of different types of flower lies in their form of symmetry. The bulk of flowers are patterned on a radial design. Ladies' smock (*Cardamine pratensis*), for example, is one of the prettiest of the spring meadow flowers. Turn the face whichever way you choose and you will find that there is no distinguishable top, bottom or side. The four petals are arranged evenly, and generally resemble each other. Compare this with bilateral symmetry in a violet, a dead nettle or a vetch, and you discover there is only one way of looking at the flower. The plane of symmetry passes through the front and rear from top to bottom. The petals and sepals also tend to differ in size and shape.

Above Wallflowers (*Cheiranthus cheiri*) are radially symmetrical or actinomorphic; whichever way the flower is bisected it will provide a pair of mirror images, because the whorls of sepals, petals, and reproductive parts are arranged evenly around 360° of the flowering axis.

The parts of a flower

At this stage you are about to be bombarded with what may seem like a depressingly large number of botanical terms. Don't be put off; once learned, these terms can be applied to any flower, and they will appear regularly in various field guides.

A flower sits atop its own stalk or *pedicel*, unless the stalk is missing in which case it is described as *sessile*.

The *Ranunculus* genus, which includes all the buttercups, possesses fairly primitive members. The central axis of the flower, called the *receptacle* or *torus*, is effectively the tip of the stalk, the shoot on which all the rest of the organs are arranged. Starting from the base of a buttercup picked off the lawn and working upwards, one encounters a circle of five greenish flaps that are quite tough and look like stunted leaves. These are the *sepals*, collectively the *calyx*, which protect the young unopened bud. Above are the most obvious features, the *petals*, again in a group of five overlapping plates. At the extreme base of each is a slightly darker, thicker area which reveals the position of the *nectary*.

Inside the whorl of sepals and petals, together called the *perianth*, lie the vital and delicate reproductive organs; the male *stamens*, bearing pollen in *anthers*, and the female *carpels* or *pistils*, each consisting of receptive *stigma* and an *ovary*, containing unfertilized seeds and connected with the stigma by a column, known as the *style*. Generally speaking, the more primitive the flower, the larger number of reproductive structures. Hence a buttercup displays a profusion of stamens and individual carpels. In a more advanced flower, such as a lily (*Lilium*) or a tomato (*Solanum*), the number of stamens is reduced, and the carpels fuse together to form an ovary with a number of cavities or *locules*.

The most complicated arrangement is found in the composite flowers, such as dandelion (*Taraxacum*). Each may appear to be a single bloom but is, in fact, an inflorescence made up of a large number of small single-petalled and sessile units called *ray florets*.

In a daisy (*Bellis*), by comparison, white or pink ray florets are arranged round the edge as visual attractants, and smaller yellow disc florets lie in the centre. The whole flower, in the case of a dandelion or daisy, is mounted on a flattened torus called the disc and surrounded, not by sepals, but *bracts* – highly specialized leaves – which make up a protective *involucre*.

Not every stem tip, of course, bears a flower. The tip is effectively the point of upward growth and many are vegetative, concerned only with the elongation of the plant and the production of leaves.

Dissecting a flower

The optimum way of recording a flower so that its structure is revealed is by drawing the half flower. To do this, lay the specimen on a pad of newspaper and bisect it with a very sharp blade, holding the whole bloom gently between your finger and thumb and drawing the blade through the tissues. If you are working with a radially symmetrical (*actinomorphic*) flower, such as a primrose (*Primula*), it can be cut in any longitudinal plane; in other words, you should cut through the stalk lengthwise, continuing through receptacle, petals and reproductive organs from back to front so that you finish up with two mirror images.

If the flower has five petals, the ideal line of bisection will divide one petal and pass between the opposite two. As a general rule, the petals and sepals alternate with each other, and because of this you will also have cut through the sepal opposite to the divided petal.

With a bilaterally symmetrical (*zygomorphic*) flower, such as a foxglove (*Digitalis*), you should make the same longitudinal cut but always in an antero-posterior plane, in other words from the top to the bottom of the flower as it rests on the plant. Again, this will produce two mirror images.

The ultimate record will include exploded drawings of the individual organs. Remember that the flower consists of whirls of highly modified leaves on a flowering axis. Using a dissecting needle and holding the flower between finger and thumb, gently tease away the outermost whirl, which will frequently consist of the green calyx sepals. This will expose the bases of the petals, which can be removed. In the primrose, the stamens will come away with the petals.

Notice that the primrose possesses five stamens; these are *opposite* to the petals, a condition known as *antipetaly*. In the foxglove, the petals have become fused so the half-whorl will come away as one piece.

Do not attempt to detach the stamens if they are positioned on the petals, but otherwise remove them carefully. The stalk will now be surmounted by a torus from which all organs except the gynoecium – ovary, style and stigma – have been removed. Notice where the gynoecium lies in relation to other parts. In many flowers, the gynoecium is at the apex with all other parts *below*; this is a *hypogynous* arrangement. In *Rubus*, for example, the organs are arranged *around* the gynoecium – *perigynous*. More rarely, for example in *Pyrus*, the torus forms a cup and the petals and sepals are arranged *on* the gynoecium – *epigynous*. Cut the ovary longitudinally to reveal its carpels and seeds, and then lay the various parts out and draw them.

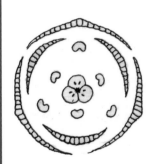 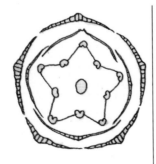

Above Parts of a flower can be drawn schematically by means of a floral diagram. This represents the essential features of the flower without the necessity for any accompanying description. It is normally accompanied by a floral formula, thus K(5) C(5) A5G (5) is the floral formula of a primrose (*Primula*). On the left is a monocotyledonous flower and right a dicotyledonous flower.

Right *Paphiopedium* sp. (Orchidaceae) typifies a bilaterally symmetrical or zygomorphic flower. Here, the inflorescence can only be bisected in one plane to provide two mirror images: from anterior (upper) to posterior (lower) surfaces.

LEAF TYPES

At one time the shapes of leaves on green plants were used as a popular identification feature, but this proved an unsound yardstick, and a scientifically accurate classification, based on flower structure, was consequently established. The pitfalls in the earlier system are not hard to find: for example, the leaves of the dead nettle *(Lamium)* and the stinging nettle *(Urtica)* may appear broadly similar in shape, hence the common name "nettle" applied to both genera, while in fact the two are from wholly distinct groups, the Urticaceae and the Labiatae, as their respective flowers show.

Nonetheless, leaves can provide a useful guide in some circumstances, and the structure of leaves will often reveal details of a plant's lifestyle. When examining a leaf, there are a number of points to watch for:

1 Does it have a stalk or petiole, or is it sessile? This is the quickest way to distinguish between the pedunculate oak *(Quercus pedunculata)* whose leaves are sessile, and the sessile oak *(Q. sessiliflora)* whose leaves are stalked ("pedunculate" and "sessile" refer to the flower structure).

2 Is the leaf simple or compound?

3 What is the leaf profile like and how is the edge patterned?

4 How is its venation (vein pattern) arranged?

5 Is the cuticle thick or thin?

6 Is there a waxy coating?

7 Is the leaf blade thin or fleshy?

8 Does the leaf surface bear hairs or spines? Are these distributed all over the leaf or in restricted areas?

Sometimes there are very specific peculiarities. You can identify a dogwood shrub *(Cornus sanguinea)* in a hedgerow through a little piece of know-how. Take a leaf and very gently pull it apart, breaking it across the direction of the main veins. Because of the peculiar elasticity of the xylem vessels you can "hang" one half of the leaf from the other by tiny threads of xylem!

Simple leaves are those in which the lamina, or leaf blade, is either entire or with marginal incisions between the veins. *Compound leaves* are those in which the lamina is not developed at all between certain major veins, thus providing a series of individual leaflets arising from the main axis.

In a simple leaf, the profile can vary considerably from a very narrow spine-like shape, as in the xerophytic (dry region) plant *Hakea*, to the broad shape of a dog violet *(Viola)*. It can also vary with the venation –

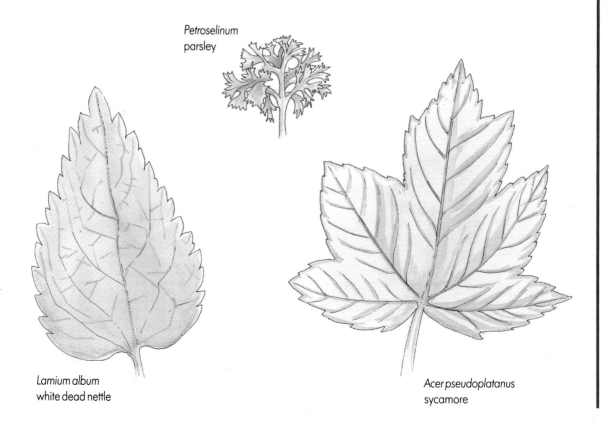

Petroselinum
parsley

Lamium album
white dead nettle

Acer pseudoplatanus
sycamore

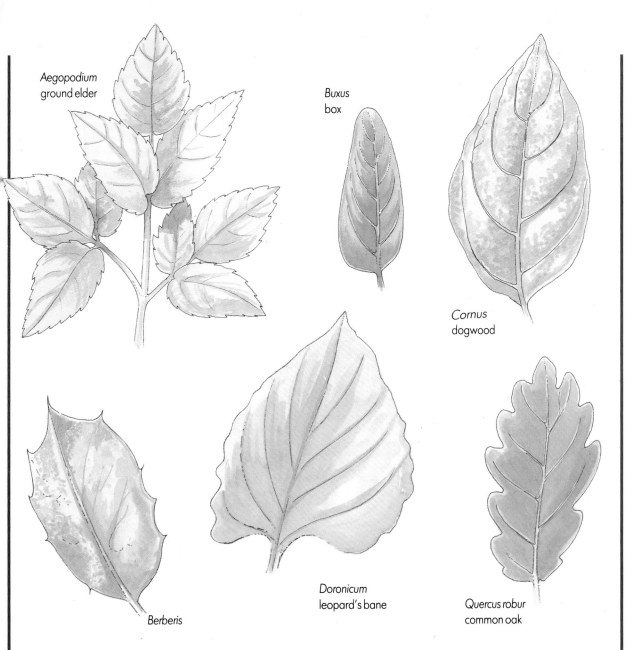

Aegopodium
ground elder

Buxus
box

Cornus
dogwood

Berberis

Doronicum
leopard's bane

Quercus robur
common oak

pinnate as in oak *(Quercus)* or palmate as in sycamore *(Acer)* or geranium *(Geranium)*. A leaf will also be characterized according to the pattern of the margin:

1 Entire (even, with no irregularities)
2 Sinuate (margin wavy)
3 Curled (margin curled)
4 Serrate (margin bears small saw-like teeth directed forwards)
5 Dentate (larger teeth pointing outwards)
6 Crenate (marginal projections not sharp but rounded)
7 Ciliate (margin fringed with fine hairs)
8 Spiny (margin fringed with spines or prickles)

Many plants, such as dogwood *(Cornus)*, protect their young leaves with a fine coating of hairs which then disappear as the leaf matures.

A fleshy leaf is generally evidence of a xerophytic plant showing an adaptation for water storage; examples of this type of plant include such succulents as the houseleek *(Sempervirum)* and the stonecrop *(Sedum)*. A waxy coating, as in the evergreen shrub holly *(Ilex aquifolium)*, is also a xerophytic modification, as is the presence of dense hairs on the leaf surface. Xerophytic adaptation can also be found in leaves that are diminutive in scale, such as the spiny leaves on a young gorse *(Ulex)*. Incidentally, the main spines on a mature plant are in fact modified *stems*.

FEEDING AND DORMANCY

The main function of the stem, apart from providing a rigid framework, is to act as a transport system, carrying water, minerals and manufactured food within the plant. Food is manufactured in all green plants by the process called photosynthesis, during which inorganic substances – carbon dioxide and water – are converted into the simple sugar, glucose, along with a vital bi-product, oxygen. The plant requires sunlight to drive the process, and the sun's energy is trapped and put to use by special microscopic structures called chloroplasts, that are located mainly in the leaf cells. These manufacture the chlorophyll that acts as catalyst for the chemical conversion process.

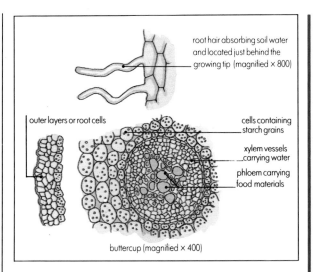

root hair absorbing soil water and located just behind the growing tip (magnified × 800)

outer layers or root cells

cells containing starch grains

xylem vessels carrying water

phloem carrying food materials

buttercup (magnified × 400)

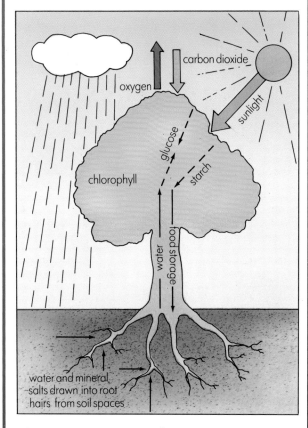

carbon dioxide

oxygen

sunlight

glucose

starch

chlorophyll

food storage

water

water and mineral salts drawn into root hairs from soil spaces

Above In a tree with a crown higher than ten metres from the ground water cannot be pumped by root pressure alone. Suction resulting from leaf transpiration draws columns of water to the top leaves.

Above right Hairs located just behind the growing tip of a root draw in water. Osmotic flow then transfers the water cell by cell to the internal "plumbing" system of the plant, known as the xylem.

Much of the movement of materials in a plant is driven by the physical phenomenon of osmosis, wherein a weak solution is dragged through a membrane (in this case the cell wall) into a stronger solution. The plant cannot readily store glucose in its tissues, because glucose is osmotically active and its presence in any concentration would throw out the whole balance of circulation, so a further series of chemical processes turns it into inactive starch, deposited in storage areas away from the "factory floor". Food materials are carried around the plant through columns of living cells that are specially equipped for the purpose and are called *phloem*.

Plants and water pressure

An unbroken column of water between roots and topmost leaves is essential. Water is the solvent in which the life processes of living things take place, and plants are no exception. Any reduction in water pressure will cause the softer parts of the plant to wilt and malfunction. The living cells only operate efficiently if they are under internal water pressure or in other words, if they are turgid. Water begins its journey from the soil by being drawn into special cells on the root tips, called root hairs. The solution in the living cells is stronger than in the soil, so the inward and upward osmotic flow is set up, creating a positive pressure in the roots. The result is a pumping action, via the internal plumbing system of water vessels, called the *xylem*, up into the stem.

This is efficient as far as it goes, but plants rarely manage to achieve a root pressure greater than one atmosphere, which will only push water to a height of 10 metres – fine for the average herbaceous plant but inadequate for a tall tree. For the water to gain further height a plant must rely on suction from the leaves, triggered by evaporation through pores in the leaf surface and known as transpiration.

The push-pull combination, coupled with the tension of the water molecules clinging to each other (the same strength that allows an insect to walk across a pond surface), is so powerful that it will draw water up to a height of 200 metres, somewhat higher than the average tree.

Dormancy

In temperate regions, the flow of water and food slows and virtually stops in the autumn, and internal activity becomes suspended during the cold dark months. In effect everything shuts down. Seasonal changes are very important in a perennial plant's annual cycle. All plants, even those growing in a tropical jungle, need periods of rest interspersed with activity.

Annuals merely produce seeds and wait to start again from scratch. In perennials, though, leaf fall is an essential and carefully contrived part of the process. In deciduous plants – those which shed their leaves each autumn – leaves do not drop off merely because they have died; leaf fall is a very deliberately contrived process. If you look at a branch which has become damaged during the summer, you will notice that the withered leaves remain attached. For leaf fall, the living leaf develops a zone of cells at the base of the stalk or petiole called the *abscission layer*, designed to rupture in the autumnal gales and frosts. Evergreens tend to shed their leaves spasmodically through the year, but there is nonetheless a constant process of loss and replenishment.

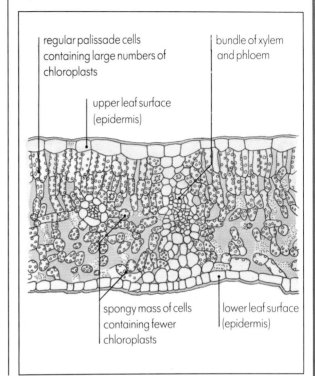

regular palissade cells containing large numbers of chloroplasts

bundle of xylem and phloem

upper leaf surface (epidermis)

spongy mass of cells containing fewer chloroplasts

lower leaf surface (epidermis)

Above right The leaves are factories for the manufacture of simple sugars from carbon dioxide and water. They use the energy of sunlight, trapped and converted to chemical energy by special organelles – the chloroplasts – located in the leaf cells. Glucose produced in the leaves is converted to inert starch for storage.

Right Plants that inhabit hedgerows often develop as "face sided". The leaves are arranged in tiers on the outer face, and all are orientated to catch the maximum amount of sunlight. If the plant's geometry is disturbed, the leaves will quickly reposition themselves.

SEASONAL CHANGES

In a small herbaceous perennial or a shrub, the obvious marks of resting, or dormancy, are leaf loss and cessation of growth, but on a stem that has become woody and thickened, the cycles of activity and rest can be seen clearly in the annual rings exposed on cut timber, and these growth rings can be used to calculate the age of a trunk. A special area of permanently young cells within the older mature stem, called the *cambium*, allows for expansion in girth without which the trunk would be unable to cope with the ever-increasing weight demands generated by stem elongation. The cambium cells repeatedly split off elements called xylem rays which very rapidly become massively impregnated with lignin and promptly die. They serve, from that juncture, to transport the enormous amounts of water needed to keep the leaves and young stems adequately supplied.

Tree rings

In temperate Europe, the peak of cambial cell division is in the spring when the xylem elements produced tend to be wide. This spring wood contrasts with that generated in autumn, when the xylem elements are denser and more compact. Annual rings can provide an accurate meteorological history; a very dry summer will severely reduce the annual band of growth for that

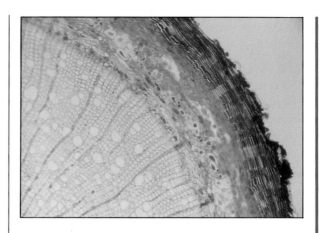

year, and a cold snap mid-season can trigger the production of dense autumnal-type growth, producing a false annual ring. Disease in the tree will be evidenced in a similar way by a temporary halt in normal growth patterns. Generally speaking, though, in a period unmarked by disease or climatic abnormality, each ring marks a complete season of the tree's history.

Buds and shoots

In a perennial plant, the stem tip, which is known botanically as the *apical meristem*, and is the region of permanently youthful tissue responsible for elongation, rests through the winter as a dormant *terminal bud*. This kind of bud is responsible for elongation growth in the main stem. Inside the sticky protective scale

Left Annual rings in a cut timber stump can be counted to establish the age of the tree. Each ring represents a year in the tree's history, though the figure can be distorted by the occasional production of false rings, due to unseasonal cold snaps or periods of disease.

Left Under the microscope, the secondary thickening of a stem is distinguished by massive development of tough lignified tissue known as xylem rays. These develop from a secondary growing zone, the cambium, which lies towards the outside of the girth.

Right In the autumn, many trees in temperate regions shed their leaves, an act which distinguishes them as deciduous species. The autumnal colours are generated through removal of green chlorophyll from the leaf cells; this allows other pigments, hitherto masked, to show through.

leaves of a horse chestnut (*Aesculus*) bud is a whole juvenile length of stem, complete with unopened leaves that overlap the apex and are telescoped together. Winter can be injurious, and the danger does not merely come from the cold. No sap is rising in the stem and the delicate tissue of the tip is at risk of drying out, and for this reason scale leaves are designed not only to afford protection against physical damage but also to keep vital moisture locked in. Most are effective merely by being tough and corky, but others develop more elaborate features. Willow (*Salix*) buds tend to be hairy on the outside, and in the horse chestnut the scales exude a sticky resin.

If you look back along the length of twig which represents last year's growth, the stem bears several give-away marks. At intervals, there are saddle-shaped scars just above which there usually arise small lateral or *axillary buds*. Each scar marks the position where a leaf fell in the autumn, and is the *abscission node*. The buds are described as axillary because they have formed in the axils of the leaves, the angle between the upper surface and the stem, and it is these buds which

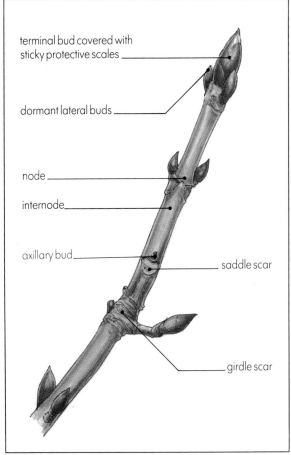

terminal bud covered with sticky protective scales

dormant lateral buds

node

internode

axillary bud

saddle scar

girdle scar

Above A winter twig of beech (*Fagus*) carries a portrait of the previous year's activity. Its oldest extremity is marked by a girdle scar, which reveals the position of the last set of terminal bud scales. Saddle scars, separated by internodes, mark the abscission points where the leaves fell in the autumn.

Above right A simple drawing is a highly effective aid to understanding the growth of a twig. The same features are detailed in a horse chestnut twig (*Aesculus*) – nodes, internodes, saddle and girdle scars, and terminal, dormant, and axillary buds.

eventually form branches on the main stem. They also provide a back-up if the main terminal bud is damaged, and not all the lateral buds automatically sprout in the spring. Some, frequently those immediately behind the terminal bud, will remain dormant indefinitely.

Between the nodes is a length of stem called the *internode*, which has expanded once the bud has opened, and if one traces the internodes back far enough, one comes across a scale or *girdle scar*. This marks the position of last year's terminal bud and was created when the scale leaves fell away from the spring shoot. Counting the girdle scars back is, like counting annual rings, a convenient way of calculating the age of a branch, or indeed of a young tree or shrub.

It is worth remembering that buds come in all shapes and sizes, from the delicate spindle-like arrangement on a beech tree, to the fat fleshy lateral bud which one eats as a sprout, or the vast terminal bud of a cabbage! All serve a similar function of protecting a developing shoot, and although they are most obvious in winter, they can arise at any time of the year.

MAKING A SIMPLE SURVEY

Having taken the briefest excursion through the botanical terms and structures you are likely to come across in the reference books and will need to distinguish on sketches and paintings, it is time to get the sun-hat or the wellies on and make a start. There is, perhaps, no better place to begin than your own back garden. If you do not have one, the yard or even the window box may well suffice.

Domestic gardens provide, ironically, one of the best environments for wild plants, however industriously one tries to deter them. In a garden, we offer a range of artificially created habitats all nudging together within a small area. There exists the open desert plateau of gravel paths and crazy paving complete with cracks and crevices, the rocky cliff face of stone walls and roofs, the regularly cropped meadow of the lawn, and the protected luxury of the herbaceous border. Even some herbicides are a boon in that, for unknown reasons, their debilitating properties towards larger weeds are actually stimulating for the growth of more primitive plants like mosses.

Equipment

What equipment do you need? The short answer is as much or as little as you choose. You can enjoy being a practical botanist with a few odds and ends collected up from around the house. We will talk about the equipment needed for drawing and painting in the next chapter, but there are one or two general accessories which will make life easier. It is a good idea to buy a plastic-covered clipboard and some clear polythene sleeves to protect your efforts against rain and mud. It is surprising how quickly things can become soggy and dirty out in the field and you will constantly be putting things down on the ground. It is also a good idea to tie your pencil or pen to a string and attach this to the clipboard or round your neck, otherwise it is guaranteed to go missing in the first five minutes.

A measure is essential, if you are going to make detailed notes. You will also need some small bottles with snap-on or screw caps – the kind of glass jars that herbs and spices come in are ideal. A pair of tweezers or forceps, some dissecting needles (to make your own, glue a pin into a pencil or a shaped piece of wood such as a kebab stick), eye droppers or pipettes and a sharp, adequately protected blade will all come in useful.

Some means of magnifying objects will also make life very much more satisfying, by revealing fine details of such organs as hairs, pores, tips of stigmas, and pollen grains. An ordinary magnifying glass will suffice up to a point, but the ideal instrument is an inexpensive jeweller's lens of the kind that you hold right up to the eye (see below), and which will provide a x10 magnification.

Right Most of the equipment that you will require for practical botany can be found around the house, or obtained from a scientific retailer. Large expenditure is not necessary – the most costly item will be the jeweller's lens. Pencils and pens, bottles, tweezers, needles, droppers, and a note pad will get you well started.

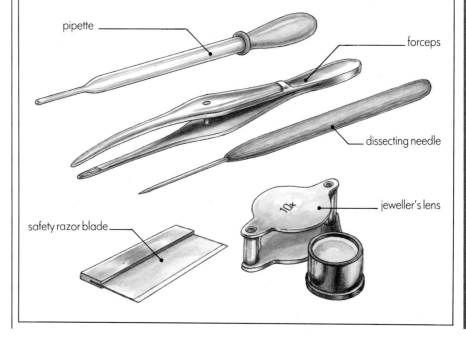

pipette

forceps

dissecting needle

jeweller's lens

safety razor blade

BOTANY IN THE GARDEN

If you have a lawn, this is a good place to head for. Some lawns are so heavily treated and manicured that they represent deserts for all but selected grasses. Most, however, contain a variety of plants known to most gardeners as weeds. So what is a weed, what is a herb, and what is a flower? These are questions which my children always ask, but in fact, there is no real botanical distinction. These are subjective terms to distinguish what is desirable or even fashionable in a garden. By way of illustration, some people will go to great lengths to remove chamomile (*Anthemis*) from their turf, classing it as a weed. Others will choose a lawn colonized wholly by chamomile, in which case it becomes a desirable plant. Fifty years ago, hedge garlic (*Alliaria officinalis*) was a herb which no self-respecting country gardener would be without. Nowadays it is generally demoted to the ignominy of being a roadside weed.

Below The common daisy (*Bellis perennis*) is one of the most familiar wild flowers in the lawn, blooming through much of the year. The lawn is an ideal place to learn the principles of botanical charting and recording.

The lawn

Later in the book, there are details about the method used to survey an area of meadow with a simple piece of apparatus called a quadrat square, but for the moment just pick an area of lawn and establish how many different plants other than grasses are growing there.

The species will vary according to the time of year, but in high summer you may be astonished at how large the list becomes. The obvious examples, all of which extend over temperate Europe, include the common daisy (*Bellis perennis*), which flowers more or less throughout the year, and the various commoner species of buttercup, including creeping buttercup (*Ranunculus repens*) and bulbous buttercup (*R. bulbosus*). You may also find dwarf thistle (*Carduus acaulis*), cut-leaved cranesbill (*Geranium dissectum*), plantain (*Plantago*), dandelion (*Taraxacum*), and many more, all growing in a rosette habit, with leaves flat to the ground and flowers on erect stems. They are typical examples of plants that will grow happily in a close-cropped meadow, but which have elected to take up residence in an artificially trimmed pasture. You have taken your first object lesson in practical botany – observing how a habitat can affect the construction of a plant, or conversely how certain constructions are more suited to a particular habitat than others.

Left Common field speedwell (*Veronica persica*) is a sprawling annual frequently found in garden flower beds. Notice the darker veins, which attract insects, luring them to the pollen.

Below Gardens offer a wide range of habitats, often within a very restricted area. Walls provide a base for mosses, lichens, and flowering plants, including pennywort (*Cotyledon*), wall rue (*Adiantum*), and stonecrop (*Sedum*). The path is a bed for other mosses and liverworts, as well as for plants that thrive on cinders, while the herbaceous border is an ideal shelter zone.

Paths, borders and walls

In the herbaceous border, you may come across a variety of wild plants ranging from perennial nettles (*Urtica*) and spear thistles (*Carduus*), to annual spurges (*Euphorbia*), poppies (*Papaver*), and ragworts (*Senecio*). Most will be opportunist species, designed to colonize bare, newly-turned soil and to beat off the types that grow more slowly. All lay root systems rapidly, those of the perennials being particularly tenacious, and the annuals being able to produce flowering stems within a few days. Contrast the more upright growths seen here with those you have seen colonizing the lawn.

Garden paths will often provide a home for mosses and liverworts, and for small matted herbs, such as pearlwort (*Sagina*). Cracks between crazy paving and other slabs will also very quickly become colonized with the type of small densely-tufted plants that would normally inhabit open rock faces. Walls will support mosses, lichens, small ferns such as wall rue (*Adiantum*), and flowering plants, including pennywort (*Cotyledon*) and stonecrop (*Sedum*), and sometimes small wiry grasses. The important point to notice is that most of these are designed to withstand drought, bearing leaves that are either reduced, tough or rubbery.

In short, there is more than enough raw material in the garden, however small, to keep the amateur botanist occupied for quite a while without ever stepping beyond the front gate!

MAKING THE RECORD
INTRODUCTION

To a point, a good field guide is an excellent means of gaining botanical experience, but to rely on it would be a passive approach, and at the end of the day you would probably find that you had absorbed very little information about the plants found and identified. Making your own record, rather than returning constantly to someone else's observations, can be a rewarding enterprise. It is a much more effective method of learning about plants and, if built up in the right way, provides a directly relevant picture which can be referred back to, and used to gain a real understanding of a habitat.

A good botanical record provides far more than just details of plant structure. It is a portfolio on a habitat, its green community, and the changes that take place there; not only in terms of space and composition, but of time, and the interactions between the individual members. It is this which turns botany from a pleasant but vicarious exploration, into a fascinating personal involvement.

Choosing the area
How much you put into the enterprise is really up to you. At one extreme, you might decide that it was worth applying for SSSI (Site of Special Scientific Interest) status or the European equivalent, to secure a disused and threatened meadow at the end of the lane, but that would involve preparing exhaustive records over at least a year. It would necessitate extensive photography, detailed identification and observation of species and subspecies, perhaps a physical herbarium – a collection of flowers and leaves – together with comprehensive accounts of seasonal variations and predation by animals.

It would demand records of the incidence of diseases, the effects of crop spraying on neighbouring fields, the possible effects of harrowing, hedge cutting and laying, and so forth. In other words, you would need a lot of energy and spare time to devote to the project. This kind of field botany is demanding and requires considerable perseverence, though on the credit side it may result in a beautiful flower meadow being preserved for posterity.

Less ambitious is a survey of a particular area of countryside, perhaps a patch of downland or forest or, equally valid, a derelict inner city site, to find out the range of plants that have become established, how many are naturally endemic and how many are introductions or escapes. You may also wish to discover the effects of pollution, and to note the ways in which plants may have modified to their environment.

On a modest scale, you can greatly enhance your understanding of plants just by making sketches and jotting down brief notes. It is surprising how rapidly this kind of exercise brings a working familiarity with details which might otherwise be taken for granted. Out

Left Practical botany can be as demanding as you wish to make it. Surveying a large area of sea cliff requires considerably more stamina than investigating the waste patch at the end of the road and may not necessarily provide any greater rewards.

enjoy it. Practical botany should be rewarding and fun – a celebration of the countryside not a labour of Hercules.

It is worth stressing again that you do not necessarily need to venture out into the wilds. One of the delights of practical botany is that you can sometimes get as much out of surveying the weeds in your back garden, a bit of old crumbling wall, a disused railway cutting, or the waste ground at the end of the street, as you can by taking a trip to some remote beauty spot. In fact you will often find more variety on a derelict urban site, and almost certainly on an old railway embankment, where some of the most astonishing ranges of wild plants grow, than you will encounter in the heart of a moorland wilderness.

Left Railway embankments are not as a rule sprayed or mown. Most people can find a disused stretch of railway not too far from home and an old cutting like this can provide an unexpected bonus with a riot of wild plants.

Below A flower meadow at Rhiniog Fawr in Wales. Many of the more remote mountain areas are only for the ambitious and the athletic. Before attempting to survey such locations you should obtain suitable walking and survival equipment.

of interest, try drawing a very common wild flower, say a field poppy, from memory. It is quite difficult to summon up details like the number of petals, the shape of the stamens, the position of the nectaries or the arrangement of leaves on the stem if you rely on the vicarious experience of field guide observation, or occasional glances at snapshot records. But having gone through the more intimate practical exercise of sketching or painting and recording details, these things are easier to recall.

Before you pack up the sandwiches and thermos flask, it is therefore worth sitting down and considering how seriously you want to take your practical botany, given your available time and inclination and, no less importantly, your physical fitness! To get the record of small rosette plants you may have to adopt a worm's eye view, spreading yourself flat on the ground on some rain-soaked hillside. Taking the perfect photograph of an epiphyte on a branch may only be possible if you climb part way up a tree. If you set out with ambitions pitched too high, you may end up frustrated and achieve nothing. Whichever option you choose,

SKETCHING AND PAINTING

The simplest, and in many respects the most reward-ing, way of making the record is by sketching. You have two options; either to draw the plant *in situ*, or to carry it to the convenience of a tray, or the table top at home.

If you decide to work with the plant where it rests, with the enormous advantage that the plant is in its natural and healthy state, there is no problem other than wriggling yourself into the right, and occasionally uncomfortable, position for work. Buy a plastic ground-sheet, incidentally, as an indispensable part of your equipment! With either of the other two options, the plant may be much easier to draw, but it will not appear wholly lifelike, and there is a serious risk of wilting or shrivelling.

An additional note of caution: once you step beyond the boundaries of your own garden, much of the European countryside is not a free playground. The land may be privately owned and, more significantly, conservation is now taken very seriously. Most coun-tries have legislation in force which makes it illegal to tamper with certain wild plants. In Britain, the number of protected plants is governed by the Wildlife and Countryside Act of 1981 which includes an expanding list of named species. It is worth checking carefully what you may or may not pick, either by purchasing a copy of the relevant laws or inspecting them at your local library. You may also find yourself in a nature reserve where local rules make it illegal to uproot or otherwise damage plants of a particular species, nationally protected or not.

Botanical drawings

Abandon aspirations to become a Monet or a Con-stable. The *Water Lilies* may look very nice hanging in the National Gallery in London, but such an ex-quisite impression does not tell you much about the botany of the plants.

A botanical record needs to arrive at a compromise between artistic aspirations and the discipline of cre-ating a scientifically accurate record. In botanical draw-ing and painting you are aiming to achieve a faithful copy of the morphology – the outward structure of the plant – down to its smallest detail.

Left To draw or paint plants in situ may mean lying flat on the ground, so a groundsheet is indispensable. Silverweed (*Potentilla anserina*) is typical of many low-growing rosette type plants.

Above The common hemp nettle (*Galeopsis tetrahit*) can be displayed in fine detail, and makes an attractive picture, by bringing it home and photographing in a studio setting. Accurate exposure and focusing are all-important.

For the simplest and most effective record, pencil drawing takes first place. It is worth investing in a good quality drawing paper, A4 (210mm × 300mm) or A5 (210mm × 150mm) format, from an art shop. Smaller than A5 risks cramped drawings with important details

Below There is great beauty to be found in the commonest of weeds. The blossoms of the bramble (*Rubus fructicosus*) are worth close inspection as subject material. A member of the rose family, its flowers are borne in panicles.

lost. Anything bigger becomes too unwieldy. Remember that you will not be popping out to the nearest beauty spot and setting up your easel. You will be hiking off the beaten track and fighting with brambles, head-high bracken, fallen trees, rocks, and the like. The amount and portability of the gear you carry is therefore quite critical. Buy a selection of art pencils; most of the time you will be working with HB and F, but it is worth including a 2H for very fine lines and a 2B or 3B used flat for shading. Soft indiarubbers, a ruler, and a set of simple dividers for measuring dimensions are all essentials. It is also worth investing in some drawing ink, together with mapping pens or a graphic pen. A spraycan of fixative, and some plastic sleeves of a size convenient to slip over your chosen format, will complete the essentials for sketching.

The pencil line drawing may not look very brilliant in artistic terms, but as a scientific record it cannot be beaten. The object of a line drawing is to record the essential features of the plant or individual structure accurately and without embellishment. It copies the plant or part of the plant as faithfully as possible by tracing the structure, both in general view, and with key areas drawn as more detailed enlargements. The result can be left as a pencil drawing or "hardened" with indian ink, but in either case a light spray of fixative will greatly assist preservation by preventing the finished result becoming smudged and grubby.

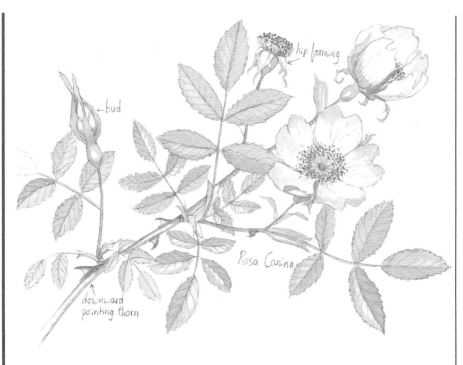

bud

hip forming

downward
pointing thorn

Rosa Canina

Left Dog rose. In a botanical drawing the anatomical details are of critical importance. The way the petals overlap, the attachment of anthers to their filaments, the arrangement of leaves; all must be carefully noted and recorded.

Right This beautiful hand-coloured engraving by Walter Hood Fitch (1817–92) is an inspiring example of what can be achieved in a botanical illustration.

Noting the details

Not all the parts need to be completed in repetitive detail. One representative drawing each of the flower bud, the open flower and a leaf will suffice, and the rest can be left in outline. There are various points to watch for and to reproduce accurately. What is the exact arrangement by which leaves arise from the stem – are they opposite each other, alternate, or in a spiral? Is the stem ribbed or smooth? Does it fork or have lateral branches? Are there hairs or spines? How are the leaf veins arranged? In the flower structure, do the petals overlap? How do the anther lobes sit atop their filaments? How many lobes does the stigma possess and how is it attached to its style? Details such as these are of secondary importance when creating a purely artistic impression, but are vital to the proper scientific record. You might not wish to hang your line drawing on the wall, but turn back to it in a year's time and it should tell you all you need to know about the plant at the moment when you captured it on paper.

To obtain a comprehensive record of the specimen, it will need to be drawn in its seedling state, and in both flowering and fruiting stages, with enlargements of immature and mature reproductive parts, seeds and, if you are really going the whole hog, the pollen. If it is a woody shrub or tree, additional sketches will reflect its overwintering state, including details of winter buds. All is designed to build up a portrait of the plant throughout the various stages of both its life and annual cycles. The line drawing can incorporate some limited shading and texture, but keep it light and never let it intrude on or mask essential details. The purist will indulge in nothing but the most discreet shading, stippling or cross-hatching on a botanical drawing, and the main structural lines should be fine, single and continuous. These are sound principles to follow.

Adding colour

The most attractive record is one that combines line drawing and watercolours. It is worth selecting the marvellous work of some of the 19th century botanical artists as a model for which to aim. They achieved portraits that are a delight to the eye and are these days very much in vogue as wall decorations, but which were, nonetheless, executed with great precision. Botanical painting should be limited to watercolours, used sparingly, and never to such an extent that the essential details are obscured. Remember that if you intend to colour a line drawing it should not include any shading or hatching. Once again, there is no necessity to colour everything. One flower and a leaf, and perhaps some other representative organs can be painted in detail, the rest can be left as a pencil or ink skeleton outline. Use of colour washes will, to an extent, obviate the necessity to write detailed notes about colour.

PHOTOGRAPHIC RECORDS

Colour photography might seem the ultimate expression, but it offers mixed blessings. One apparent advantage lies in the notion that it provides an extremely accurate general view of the plant, but it is false security to base a record exclusively on photographs. The result may be aesthetically very satisfying, but it will not provide as much detailed information as you might imagine, and it will need to be supported by notes and sketches if it is to serve the purpose. Good technique can, needless to say, vastly enhance the effectiveness of photographs as a botanical record.

An ultra-simple camera with a separate view finder is fine for holiday snaps and general views, but it does offer risks when you want precise composition in close-up because of the problems of parallax, in which the viewfinder offers a slightly different framing of the scene to that of the lens. Not all cameras with separate viewfinders are compensated for parallax, and you may end up with vital parts of the composition missing.

Which camera?

SLR (single lens reflex) cameras are ideal for the practical botanist, but it is worth bearing in mind that while the computerized models on offer these days may take much of the work out of photography, the more gadgetry that is built into the instrument, the less subjective control is left with you. The camera's computer is never able to reason quite as subtly as the human brain!

A professional photographer will still use a separate, hand-held, exposure meter, and there are sound reasons for this. Imagine that you are composing a shot of some very brightly-lit whitish flowers against the background of a dark hedge. There is a risk that through-lens metering will register the dark background in preference to your subject, with the result that the foreground will be over-exposed and burnt out. If you shoot a vista of blooms against a bright sky, you may end up with the reverse effect. In both instances the camera's meter has misread the situation. With an independent meter, you can establish the proper degree of exposure, and you will also have the advantage of being able to calculate necessary exposure with greater accuracy, by directing the meter back towards the camera and measuring the incident light reaching the subject.

On similar grounds, it is better to have control over your chosen point of focus and depth of field, rather than fully automated focusing. The best option is an SLR camera which provides you with full manual operation as and when you choose, but above all it should be one that you can understand and operate easily out in the field. The odds are that you will continue to use the Nikon, Pentax or model that you are familiar with, but if you are buying a new camera there are a few useful tips to follow. In the first place, make sure that it is not too heavy, and that it is robust in action. Remember, this instrument is going to follow you up hill and down dale in all weathers. It is also essential that the camera has a facility allowing you to interchange lenses rapidly and easily. The type of lens

Left Shooting a subject against a bright sky can prove a hazard for the unwary photographer. Make sure that your exposure is sympathetic to the subject, not the background, or there is a serious risk of under exposure.

Above left Most cameras are sold equipped with a standard 50mm focal length lens. This is fine for the majority of snapshots but additional lenses, not necessarily at high cost, may be desirable.

Above right An ultra-wide macro attachment which screws on to the front of a 50mm lens provides an inexpensive way of obtaining close-up shots.

mounting is probably not critical, because modern accessory manufacturers, such as Zeiss, Vivitar and Tamron, supply adaptors to fit most camera bodies, but if you intend to continue using your old camera make sure that you can obtain the necessary adaptors to take modern lens fittings.

Lenses

Your camera will be equipped with a lens of normal 50mm focal length unless you specify otherwise. This is perfectly adequate for general shots of plants and for most broad views, but if you require to fill the frame with any object smaller than about 20cm, additional equipment is needed. The ideal option, at least in theory, is to have a selection of macro-lenses, which permit you to shoot the tiniest part of the plant full-frame. This, however, is an extremely costly exercise and it also results in a very heavy and cumbersome load of camera gear.

I possess two invaluable lenses to complement my 50mm workhorse. One is an ultra-wide + macro attachment. This takes about ten seconds to screw on to the front of the 50mm, and effectively allows me to get within 10cm of my subject, filling the frame with an area about 14cm across.

The second provides the key to the really massive enlargement of tiny features. It is a 2 x macro focusing teleconverter, made by Vivitar, which fits between the standard lens and camera body. At the end of its

focusing range, an object measuring only 30mm will fill the picture, providing a 1:1 enlargement, with excellent resolution. A problem with most macro lenses is that one has to position the camera very close to the subject, which can make lighting tricky, but an added beauty of the macro teleconverter combination is that the tip of the lens is still positioned no nearer to the subject than 10cm. The Vivitar attachment is readily available, and at a cost about half that of a purpose-built macro lens it is a worthy addition to your kit.

At the other end of the scale, an 80-200mm zoom lens is an invaluable tool. It will allow you to take good pictures of trees and areas of landscape, eliminating much unnecessary foreground without having to struggle into shooting positions which may be virtually inaccessible. Remember, though, when using any "long" lens or lens combination that the light reaching the film surface may be reduced. A wider aperture or slower exposure may be needed.

Below A macro-focusing teleconverter is probably the most economical route to obtaining massive enlargement of subject material without going to the expense of special macro lenses.

FILM TYPES AND FLASH

In choosing film there are, of course, a great many permutations available. Assuming that you intend to work in colour, the first consideration must rest between reversal stock for transparencies and negatives for prints. There are advantages and disadvantages with both, and the choice is down finally to personal preference and to what you intend doing with the results. It is worth mentioning, though, that the two types of stock do not always behave in the same way. Reversal film tends to be less tolerant of contrasted light and shade. Using negative stock, you can take a quick shot of plants growing on a dappled woodland floor and achieve a good, well-balanced result. Shoot

Above Colour reversal stock for transparencies can generate badly contrasted pictures particularly, as here, in dappled shade.

the same scene with reversal film and the picture that emerges can be badly contrasted between extremes of burn-out and under-exposure.

Because you will often be working in less-than-ideal conditions of light and may wish to achieve big close-up framing, all of which points to the need for bigger exposure times or wider apertures, it is important to select the correct film speed. A few years ago, high-speed colour film tended to produce coarse-grained results; nowadays, you can use an ISO 400 (DIN 21) rated stock, and even higher, without loss of fine detail.

Left It is important to choose a film stock which gives you authentic natural colours. This view of Sheffield Park in Sussex was shot on Kodak film which is excellent for the purpose.

Above It is only in recent times that high speed colour film has been "cured" of excessive graininess. This photograph of *Symphytum officinalis* is typical of the problem which used to occur at ISO 400 or above.

more one can shoot in the first hours after sunrise the better. The general rule should be to avoid taking pictures in the middle of the day because at this time the light is hard and flat. Late afternoon is also risky, with colours tending to take on a more orange cast because of the build-up of dust in the air.

The instinct may be to place the camera with the sun at your back, but sometimes a better result will be achieved by using sunlight from a more subtle direction. While the light source cannot be aligned directly behind the subject without causing flare, if you can orientate it to a position between 9.0 o'clock and 3.0 o'clock, side or a degree of back illumination will give flowers a luminous, almost translucent appearance, and can pick up fine details that might be missed with more direct, flat lighting.

When photographing a plant *in situ*, it is sometimes quite difficult to distinguish the subject adequately from a jungle of extraneous foliage, particularly if it is growing adjacent to a hedge, but if the light source can be angled so as to place the background in shadow, the subject is picked out with greater definition.

Above Choosing the right time of day is important, when setting out to take pictures of flowers. In early morning the air is clear, and slanting sunlight can magically enhance an otherwise dull picture.

Right Wild marjoram (*Origanum vulgaris*) looks yellowish in this photograph because it was taken in late afternoon. The dust-laden air has an adverse effect on the colour accuracy.

If I need transparencies of botanical subjects my own preference is daylight Fujichrome 400 or Kodak Ektachrome 400, and if I wish to generate prints, Fujicolor 400 or Kodacolor Gold 400. Both stocks are readily available in most European countries, giving consistently good results when used correctly, and the standard of processing is generally excellent.

Light
The quality of the available light, and the way in which it is exploited, can make a world of difference, not only to the artistic quality of the photograph, but also to the amount of botanical detail revealed. In winter, beggars cannot be choosers, but on good summer days the

TRIPODS AND FOCUSING

It is very tempting to use artificial light from a flashgun in dull conditions or under gloomy woodland canopies, but this is not to be recommended. Unless you can flood the whole area with illumination, and can also place the source where you need it, flash provides uneven density and, in any case, can do nasty things to subtle colour tints. Hence, one other piece of essential photographic equipment is a tripod, which will enable you to utilize low level daylight by allowing exposure times longer than 1/50th of a second. It is unnecessary to go to elaborate and expensive extremes in choosing a tripod, the only limiting criteria being that, like the camera, it must be robust, simple to operate and compact.

The quintessence of a good and effective photograph – and botanical subjects are no exception – lies in accurate focusing and in selecting of appropriate depth of field. Essentially, the shorter the distance between camera and subject, the more precise the focusing adjustment, and when you are working with the macro lens, a few millimetres of adjustment either way can make or mar a photograph. Generally speaking, the camera will need to be set up fairly close to the subject to provide full-frame pictures of most of the herbaceous annuals and smaller perennials, and therefore the focusing will be quite critical.

A few minutes of careful consideration over the plant you are about to capture on film is well worthwhile. Decide which are the most important features. If you want to capture the details of the flowers, for example, choose a bloom that is facing the camera and is in perfect condition, and use it as a focal point. It should, ideally, be situated not too far forward or back on the flowering head. With a long-stemmed plant the camera should, if possible, be angled so that both the top and bottom of the subject are roughly equidistant from the lens, otherwise the flowers may seem to be rearing in a peculiar manner from fuzzy green space. By the same token, if the plant has projecting lateral branches, try to arrange the shot so that the major ones lie parallel to the focal plane.

Depth of field

The next consideration must be the depth of field. Most lenses are calibrated to show the limits at each f-number. The closer to the subject, the smaller the degree of depth which will be seen in sharp focus. With small subjects taken at very close range, the depth of

Above When selecting a subject make sure that it is angled towards the camera in such a way as to retain as much as possible of the structure in sharp focus. Use a bloom facing the camera as your focal point.

field is far more critical than if one is photographing an oak tree from 30 metres. Ideally, one is looking for maximum depth of field when working in macro dimensions, to achieve which requires a lens aperture of f22 or f16. Stopping down any lower will result in a picture that is perhaps four-fifths out of focus. This provides a further reason for owning a tripod and using a reasonably fast film stock, because you may frequently require exposure times in the order of ½ second or more.

If the maximum depth of field is desirable for a tiny subject, you will discover that it is sometimes of less advantage if you are trying to separate a plant from its background. By using a wide aperture to create limited depth of field, it is often possible to throw the background into soft focus and thus bring out the main subject more keenly.

One final point: never be satisfied with just one shot. Always take at least two with varying exposures and angles. It may seem an extravagance but it is an essential insurance policy.

f2.8

focusing on tree in near-distance with aperture wide results in very narrow depth of field.

f2.8

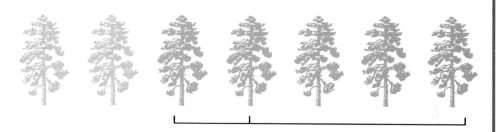

focusing on tree in middle-distance with aperture wide results in 1 tree in front of point of focus sharp, and 3 trees behind.

f2.8

focusing on infinity with aperture wide results in more of foreground not being in focus.

f11-f22

focusing on middle-distance with lens aperture stopped down gives much greater depth of field.

DRYING AND PRESERVING

No botanical record is really adequate without specimens of the plant to accompany the notes and illustrations, although if you are going to collect material for drying and preserving, remember to check whether or not you are legally entitled to pick, and then take only the minimum requirement.

Drying

Drying is the usual option. The techniques vary according to the type of material, but there are one or two general rules. During summer, the ideal time to collect is on a dry morning, just after the dew has evaporated. If this is not possible, shake off as much surplus moisture as you can. If you are collecting ripe seed heads, don't be tempted to let them dry naturally on the plant. Controlled conditions indoors, away from insect pests and mildews, will produce better results. Once collected, the objective is to dry the material as rapidly as possible in the dark, in this way minimizing fading and shrivelling.

The airing cupboard is probably your most convenient drying chamber. Hang drying, which retains the

Below A flower press to use at home need not involve a costly purchase. A simple but effective apparatus can be constructed from pieces of plywood which are tightened by means of bolts and butterfly nuts, all available from local hardware stores.

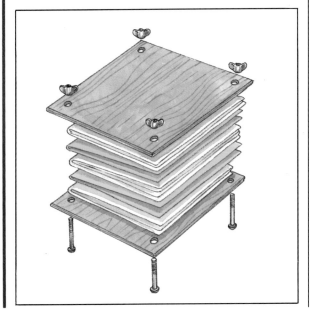

three-dimensional appearance of the specimens, is best done by suspending the material upside down in a free circulation of air. Grasses and other delicate materials should be laid out flat on a tray covered with brown paper, or across the wooden slats of the cupboard. The best option for flowers, leaves and small whole plants is pressing.

Pressing

Most of us will remember happy if not entirely successful childhood experiments with wild flowers, bits of newspaper, and a pile of books. The most important ingredient for success with pressing is patience, because it takes at least five or six weeks for the process to reach a point where the material is fixed and drying can continue for up to a year. It is no good taking sneak previews, unless the material is bulky and you think that the absorbent layer may need replacing. The rule is that the longer you leave the drying and pressing, the thinner and more permanent will be the result and the lower the risk of serious fading.

Use blotting paper rather than newspaper, as the latter tends to leak its print on to the material. Lay the plant specimen carefully between two sheets backed by pieces of cardboard and stack a weighty pile of books on top. It is as simple as that. The only restriction is that the material needs to be truly pressed flat. If it is at all bulky, the absorbent paper will not come into proper contact, and the stem or flower head may rot.

You can, of course, proceed to more elaborate presses, either purchased commercially, or homemade. The latter can be made from 30cm-squares of bonded plywood, corrugated cardboard and blotting paper, all compressed with screws and butterfly nuts. A press of this type is very simple to construct and will undoubtedly cost a great deal less than the shopbought version.

Desiccants

A further option, for use with very delicate flowers, is to immerse the material in a chemical desiccant. The results tend not to last as long as air-dried or pressed flowers, but desiccants will generally preserve the colours more accurately than the other methods. Commercial or household borax powder is ideal. Using a plastic sandwich box with an airtight lid, sprinkle in about 2cm of borax, then lay the plants on the powder so that they do not touch each other and gently shake on more borax until the specimens are covered completely to a depth of a further 2cm. It is important to shuffle the box as you add the powder to

make sure that it has found its way into all the nooks and crannies. Seal the box, taping round the join of base and lid, and leave it for about three days, depending on the bulk of material to be desiccated. If the specimen is fully dried out it should feel crisp. It is important, when the plant is removed, to brush away as much borax as possible from around leaves and petals.

Glycerine preservation

Becoming a practical botanist does not prevent you from revelling in the plants you are studying just for their sheer beauty. One delightful method of retaining an even more lifelike record than dried or pressed plants is glycerine preservation. The results can be most attractive, though glycerined specimens are not really suitable for a herbarium. Glycerine embalming replaces the natural fluids in the plant by glycerine, which then acts as a preservative, keeping the tissues soft and supple in a way that drying and pressing does not allow. Colours tend to become richer and deeper. Glycerine impregnation only works effectively with certain kinds of plant material, and is not really suitable for very delicate specimens. It is particularly good, though, for twigs with berries, for any flower heads that tend to retain their shape when dried, and for the stronger, self-supporting leaves like those of blackberry (*Rubus*), thyme (*Thymus*) or helleborines (*Helleborus*), as well as those of virtually all trees, broad-leaved and coniferous.

Remove any damaged parts of the material. If the stem is tough or woody, split it for about 3cm up from the cut base and, when necessary, peel off the bark to about the same length. Choose a narrow container and fill it to a depth of about 10cm with a mixture of one-third glycerine to two-thirds hot water. When cool put the specimens in the container and leave them for from one to six weeks, depending on their size and the thickness of their leaves.

STORAGE AND PRESENTATION

Once prepared, irrespective of the method, it is essential to keep the herbarium material dry. Bringing it back into a damp atmosphere will only begin a reversal of the process. Store your herbarium specimens in a dry place, and in individual envelopes. Ideally, each storage box should include a small bag of desiccant crystals, such as ground silica gel.

The European centre of dried herbarium material is located in the Royal Botanic Gardens at Kew in England. The basis of the collection was assembled during the British Empire period, when globe-trotting colonials sent back plant material from all over the world. Kew herbarium now houses some six million dried specimens and the number is still growing year by year. Subject to agreement, Kew will verify the identity of herbarium material of which you are unsure against their own records.

Montages

Dried and pressed flowers make lovely wall decorations, and you may decide to combine useful cataloguing with the fun of making montages. Instead of making a picture based solely on aesthetic considerations, try grouping plants together according to taxonomy and habitat.

All kinds of material can be used as a montage base, from cardboard to cork or even polystyrene, but choose something that has a pleasant-looking texture and one that you can live with. The choice of framing is entirely personal. Generally speaking, pressed material is easier to work with than air-dried plants. First draw out the arrangement that you intend to create. This is important because once it has been stuck in place, the material is more or less impossible to remove without serious damage. It is best to start applying the specimens to the base from the centre and then work outwards, perhaps placing the largest shapes in the middle of the pattern. Stick them down with a fast-acting adhesive and hold any large specimens in place for a few minutes with a small weight.

Right You can use various methods for preserving flowers. (**a**) Place flowers on strips of cardboard bent into corrugations and fill container with desiccant. (**b**) Small flowers such as daisies can be dried in desiccant. (**c**) Dry tall flower spikes in a paper or plastic cup filled with desiccant. (**d**) Keep air-dried flowers upright and separate with chicken wire.

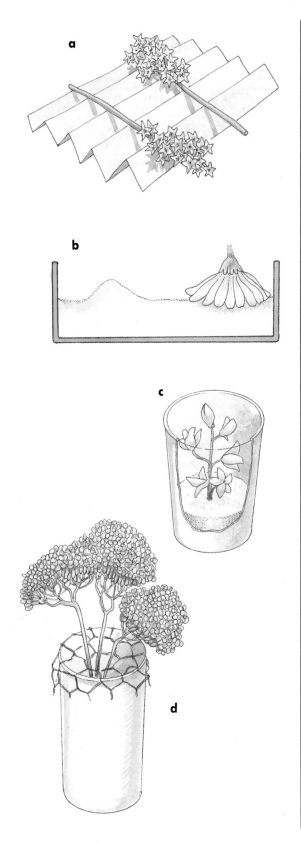

These examples of pressed flower montages are an indication of the effects which can be achieved on a purely aesthetic level. The backgrounds and frames should be carefully selected to complement the flowers.

CATALOGUING

All the methods of keeping a visual record are valuable up to a point. They will, however, reveal little about the plant's growth pattern, its times of dormancy, its flowering period and seeding, the conditions it needs for growth, its relationship with other plants, and its aggressiveness or lack of it within the community. These things will be revealed only through written details. You have to decide, therefore, whether to include your drawing, painting or dried material as part of an integrated record, or whether to keep separate catalogue cards containing written details only, which will then lead you quickly to the illustrative material. There are several ways of approaching cataloguing, and it is really a matter of deciding which is best suited to your kind of practical botany.

If you are merely interested in building a taxonomic library, in other words an encyclopaedia of plants according to their biological grouping, then you will need to arrange your records on the lines of botanical classification, dividing all plants into Monocotyledones and Dicotyledones, and then into families, genera and ultimately species. In other words, you will be doing more or less that which the field guide does, but with the great satisfaction that it is all your own work. Following the layout of the field guide that you have chosen to adopt as a manual is no bad thing, because you will become familiar with a particular lay-

out and ordering. Most field guides tend to open the list of Dicotyledones with the Ranunculus family and close with the more sophisticated groups like the Compositae.

You do not have to follow this arrangement. There is nothing to stop you cataloguing flowers by colours. While this is not quite so convenient scientifically, it may suit your purpose. It is probably still worth separating plants into family groups however, even if you are following colour schemes. Alternatively, you may decide to catalogue according to habitat. All the plants found growing in a limestone pavement would

Slide 401. Box3.

SAPONARIA OFFICINALIS (Soapwort)
(Caryophyllaceae) pink family   Introduced for cultivation

July 16 1989   Park, Worthing Sussex
adjacent to old elm stump in rough grass

10" high   flowers- 1" across pale pink.

2 Styles
Capsule opens into 4 teeth.

Above Montages of dried flowers and leaves provide not only an attractive decoration, but a useful botanical record. Flowers may be grouped according to family relationships, or habitats.

Left The record entered on to a catalogue card may not seem particularly exciting at the time but it is probably one of the most important aspects of practical botany. It is all too easy to forget significant details unless they are written up.

be assembled together, for example, and separated from those growing on a high moorland. Your target may be to become an authority on water plants, in which case cataloguing may be based on habitat, or on the means by which plants become adapted to a hydrophytic or water-bound life.

The essentials are to provide the plant with its correct Latin name and its common title, the date on which you found it, the exact location, labelling for all the points of interest, and any notes that you feel will complement the record. You might, for example, note

The arum lily (*Arum maculatum*) provides a striking example of the necessity of making records at different stages of a plant's flowering and fruiting. The inflorescence (**below**) consists of a dense spike or spadix of female flowers at the base, male flowers above, and a purplish club-shaped top, partly surrounded by a leafy bract, the spathe. The fertilized flowers (**right**) mature and ripen into bright red berries in a short spike atop a bare peduncle. By this stage the leaves and spathe have died away. To the uninformed there seems little to relate the two stages of growth.

that the plant was growing in a windswept position, or in an area regularly cropped by grazing animals, or beside a trackway, or included as part of an ancient hedge system.

Whichever method of cataloguing you adopt, plan it in advance and start as you mean to go on. A potentially disastrous mistake is to imagine that you can go back over your work and catalogue it at the end of the season. The worst result of a year's hard work is to end up with a pile of drawings and notes with no means of sorting and accessing them. You may imagine that you will remember all the details, and will be able to put your hand instantly on the specimens you recorded on the trip to the Algarve last summer, but the exercise may be harder than you think. The golden rule is to record the details at the time, when the plant is *in situ* and alive. Never rely on memory. The advice is particularly apposite when it comes to photographic records. It is so easy to shoot several rolls of film, thinking that everything can be labelled when the photographs come back from processing. It never works, and you are left to gaze at beautiful but anonymous masterpieces!

MICROSCOPY

Microscopic examination of the plant pollen, hairs, and other micro-structures as well as the internal anatomy of plants is an important part of practical botany. An elaborate microscope is not an essential piece of equipment but, as with binoculars or a camera, the quality of optical resolution is critical, and you tend to get what you pay for. Even a simple microscope with good lenses can be quite expensive, and you will also require some other specialized bits and pieces to enable you to prepare the slides for inspection. As a result, you should view microscopy as a longer-term investment. A list of the necessary basic materials, available through scientific equipment retailers, is provided at the end of this section. Of necessity this is a very brief introduction to microscopy, and if you decide to pursue the techniques any further it is advisable to invest in a good, easy-to-read, beginners' manual on plant micro-technique, of the type available from academic or scientific bookshops.

With a microscope, magnifications are possible far in excess of the ×10 available with the jeweller's hand-lens, but the material must be properly prepared. Unless it is very small it must be "cleared" by making it sufficiently thin and removing any opacity to allow light to shine through it, rather like a photographic transparency. If you fail to render the subject transparent all you will see is a dark featureless blob. In addition, staining is often required in order to make delicate structures readily visible.

Preparing slides

The preparation of a permanent slide involves four essentials: in the first place, the material must be fixed, to prevent decomposition, after which it can be stained; the third stage is to clear the material, after which it can be mounted on the slide. If the material is not intended for a permanent preparation, the first stage is obviated and the last is made simpler. If you are making a temporary slide, it is best to start by looking at whole mounts – pollen, nettle hairs, root hairs and so on, which are tiny enough to be deposited on a glass slide whole and gently pressed under a cover slip.

Most clearing agents, such as clove oil, are non-miscible with water, and since plant material contains water, the options are either to remove this by chemical dehydration or to use a water-miscible agent such as lactophenol, which is composed of equal parts of phenol crystals, lactic acid, glycerin, and distilled water. This is an ideal substance for beginners, and if mixed with a general dye such as aniline blue it will provide good temporary preparations of some botanical materials.

An alternative method is to use a general stain such as haematoxylin, dissolved in water. This is applied for five minutes, after which it is partially

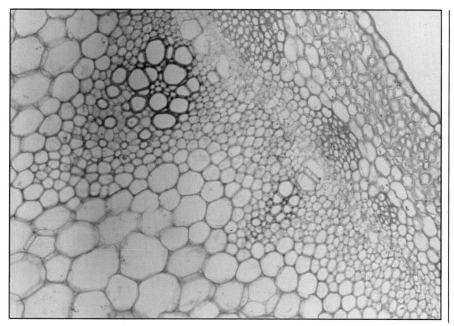

Left A transverse section through the young herbaceous stem reveals details of the anatomy. Bundles of xylem vessels and some strengthening tissue are stained red. The living cells (including food conducting phloem) are green.

Right The root of a herbaceous plant contains none of the photosynthetic cells but, in addition to xylem and phloem elements, possesses simple cells which store starch grains.

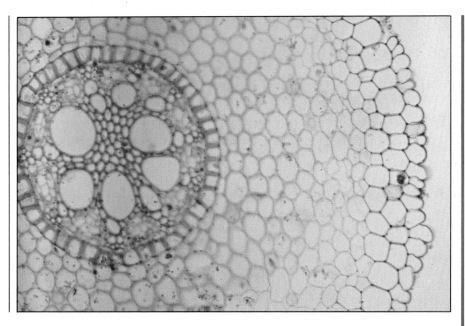

Below Sections are cut on very accurately built slicing machines known as microtomes. This sledge microtome is being used to cut sections of a buttercup stem compressed between slices of cork. Each section will be no more than 30 microns thick.

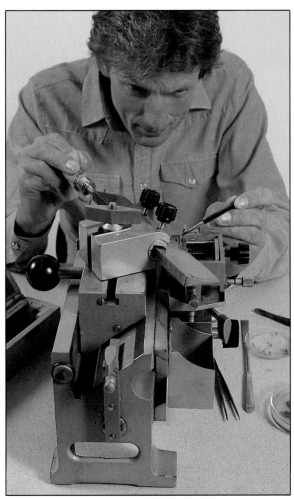

washed out by flooding the material with a weak 10 per cent vinegar solution until a pale red tint is achieved. Next, the material must be "blued" by removing the acid solution and replacing it with tap water. The preparation can then be mounted in a clearing agent such as glycerine. If, however, any but the firmest materials are plunged straight into glycerine, they will shrivel. To avoid this, you must first make up a solution of 10 per cent glycerine with water. Add the material to a small quantity of the solution; cover it lightly to exclude dust, and then stand it in a warm place until the water has more or less evaporated. Finally, mount the material in pure glycerine.

Sections
Most larger items, such as stems and roots, will need to be sectioned into very thin slices. Professional sections are cut on a machine, but you can easily produce quite good sections by hand. Find a good quality bottle cork which does not have a very dark, gritty texture and cut off two small flat pieces, each about 1cm × 1cm × 3mm. You are going to create a miniature sandwich, using the cork to steady the material that you intend to prepare. Score a small V-shaped groove right across one face of each cork piece. Lay a small fresh length of herbaceous stem – choose something reasonably firm to begin with such as ivy (*Hedera*) or lime (*Tilia*) – between the cork sandwich so that about a 2mm stub is poking out. Take a brand new safety razor blade and, holding

the cork sandwich firmly between your finger and thumb and keeping the stem or root section vertical, draw the edge of the blade diagonally across the material with a deliberate single gliding stroke to remove the stub. Now repeat the action, trying to take the thinnest possible slices of cork. Float the sections in a small dish of water using an artist's paintbrush. After a little practice you will find that you are producing sections of cork, plus the vital material, which can be stained and will prove sufficiently thin to examine under the microscope.

Permanent preparations need killing, or fixing, first. There is a variety of reagents on the market, the

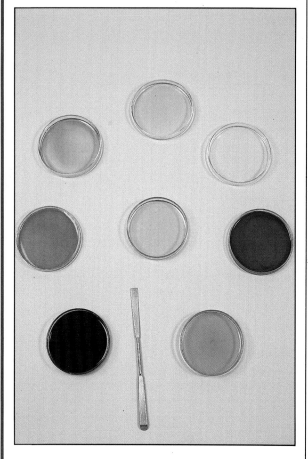

Above Thin sections of tissue are transferred through various solutions, including a red stain (safranin) and green or blue (FCF fast blue), and alcohol to dehydrate them before clearing and mounting on glass slides.

Right Leaves take considerable skill to section effectively without a cutting microtome. This Prunus section would not be possible unless by a very expert hand, but it is worth trying something more compact such as lavender or holly.

simplest of which, though crude, is an aqueous solution of 70 per cent industrial methylated spirits (IMS). One of the best general plant fixatives, however, is FAA (formalin-aceto-alcohol), which can be obtained from a scientific supplier or perhaps from a friendly college. Small pieces of the plant material must be immersed in the solution for at least 24 hours before use. The cutting technique which follows is just the same as that already described, though the material must first be rinsed under the tap.

After you have made your sections, you can then stain them with haematoxylin, but a more sophisticated technique is to use two stains, safranin which colours woody (lignin) tissue red, and a light green or blue counterstain for all the remaining tissues. Sections can be mounted temporarily by placing them in a 10 per cent glycerine solution and allowing this to evaporate, but permanent mounting in a substance such as Canada balsam is more satisfactory. The technique entails first dehydrating the stained sections by flooding them with grades of IMS, starting with 30 per cent and continuing with 50, 70, 90, 95, 100 per cent solutions, leaving them in each grade for about 2 minutes, and then clearing the dehydrated sections in clove or cedarwood oil before placing them on their slides, covering each with a drop of mountant, sealing with a coverslip, and drying out in a warming oven.

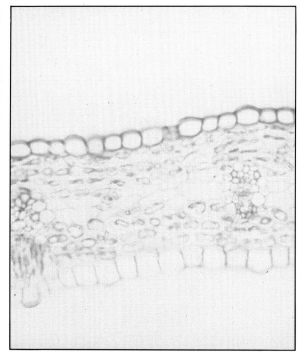

Materials for microscopy

The following is a list of the basic items that you will need in order to make worthwhile use of microscopy.

Microscope offering eyepiece magnifications of ×8 or ×10 and objective magnification of ×3, ×10, and ×40. (Daylight illumination will be cheaper than the built-in variety.)
Glass slides measuring 75mm × 25mm
Coverslips 19mm round
Slide labels
Watch glasses (minimum of 4)
Alcohol IMS (may incur excise duty)

Distilled water
Acetic acid (vinegar) or dilute hydrochloric acid
FAA fixative (caution – formaldehyde fumes are toxic)
Glycerine
Lactophenol
Cotton blue or aniline blue stain (in lactophenol)
Haematoxylin (aqueous)
Safranin (aqueous)
Fast green or blue (alcoholic)
Clove or cedarwood oil (sunflower oil is not so good)
Canada balsam or proprietary mountant (some are aqueous)
Cork
Razor blades
Fine art paintbrush for handling sections
Small bottles for fixation and preservation of material

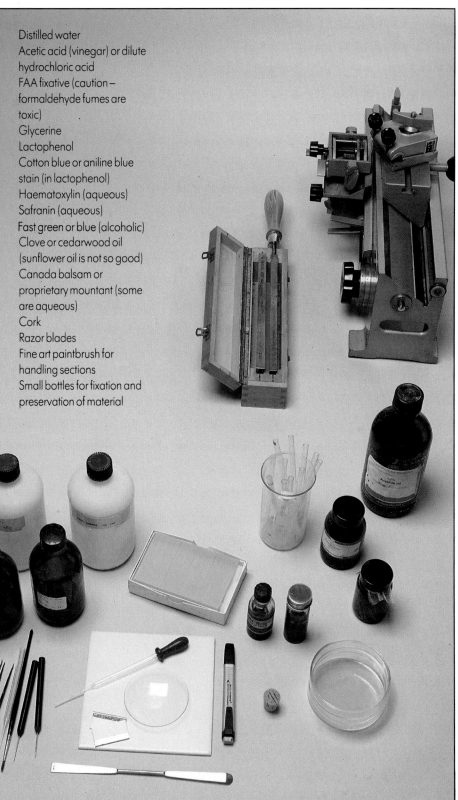

WOODLAND FLOWERS AND TREES
INTRODUCTION

Between 10,000 and 15,000 years ago, when the last Ice Age was in retreat, as much as 60 per cent of Europe became clothed by forest. The process began with the icy tundra, which supported colonies of scrub vegetation. On the lower and more protected ground this evolved into the northern pine forests. Further south, the soils and climate supported mixed woodlands of oak, alder, hazel and wych elm, and in due course beech and the other more recent arrivals, many of which were spread artificially by man, were added to these. On the hills, the broad-leaf woodlands gave way to pine, birch and juniper. As the climate became warmer, so the coniferous forests retreated and broad-leaf trees advanced further north, but at this juncture man began to play an increasingly significant role in shaping the landscape.

Old and new woodlands

Across Europe, very little of the ancient woodlands is left. Roman writers described the Hercynian forest that stretched as far as one could travel east of the Rhine. Italy was once clothed almost from the Alps to the tip of Naples with oak forests; almost all are gone, though patches remain in such areas as the Tuscan hills. In the British Isles, likewise, there exist scattered remnants of

Below An open birch wood is about the nearest you will find to original primitive woodland. Birch and hazel were among the earliest trees to colonize the open tundra, and after a fire they are still among the pioneering species.

ancient forests: for example, patches can be found of the ancient Caledonian forest which once enveloped much of Scotland. Some 10,000 years ago, Ashdown forest covered 14,000 acres of south-east England with, as its name suggests, a dominant overcoat of ash trees, but now only 6,000 acres survive. From long before the time of the Romans, successive generations have chopped down the woodlands to create fields and pastures, and to provide fuel and housing timber. Since the industrial revolution, demands have accelerated the process mightily.

The botanist venturing out into countryside almost anywhere in Europe is meeting with a man-made environment, and the woodlands are no exception. The densely-packed plantations of conifers that characterize so much of today's forested landscape bear little similarity to their ancient counterparts. When plantation trees are young, the habitat is thickly colonized. The ground supports a profusion of grasses, brambles, willow herb, and shrubs like bilberry (*Vaccinium*), or, when the soil is acidic, heathers and bracken. But as the trees grow up, most of the undergrowth plants are stifled. Virtually no light penetrates the tight ranks of mature spruce, fir, and larch, and the soil is made so acidic by the fallen needles that little could survive even if the canopy were less dense.

Above Conifers have been planted extensively in Europe as a cash crop. Little grows beneath their dense canopies and the soil becomes very acid.

Right The English South Downs were once covered extensively by forests of beech, though very few areas remain wooded, the best known being the "rings", such as Cissbury and Chanctonbury in Sussex.

The woodland environment

A natural woodland, whether of coniferous or broad-leaf trees, is a comparatively open landscape consisting of dominant species interspersed with glades and patches of scrub. The tree canopy covers a series of layers known as under-storeys, and these descend through immature trees and shrubs down to tall, intermediate, and finally low-growing herbaceous plants that clothe the woodland floor. The degree of gloom varies, of course. In some beech woods, shading is fairly uniform, while in remnants of the old natural pine forests conditions are almost park-like. Open mixed woodland provides protection for delicate plants, abundant climbing frames, nutritious, humus-rich soil, increased atmospheric humidity and water-supply, and in the glades and at the woodland edge, the additional benefits of a sunlit and airy pasture environment.

The dominant, naturally-occurring trees in any area of woodland will tend to be determined by the soil type. Hence a siliceous, well-drained soil will promote sessile oak (*Quercus*), whereas a calcareous soil will often favour ash (*Fraxinus*), and these dominant species will, in turn, regulate the type and quality of the undergrowth.

BEATING THE TREES

If there is a single outstanding disadvantage to herbaceous plants and shrubs taking up residence in a woodland, it is the potential lack of light. The leaf canopy opens across Europe at different times, but in the middle temperate latitudes the process is probably complete around the end of April. Where a woodland has been planted on pastureland, the undergrowth species will, for a time, be those of a grassland, but sooner or later they will be ousted by species better able to tolerate deep shade. Conversely, typical woodland plants will survive for a time after trees have been cut down, but will eventually be replaced by species suited to open pasture.

Some plants have become well-adapted to a woodland life by gearing their annual cycles of flowering and growth to beat the arrival of the tree canopy. Spring

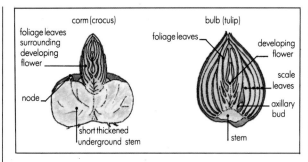

Above The crocus corm is a compacted underground stem or rootstock which acts as a storage organ to nourish the emerging leaves and flowers. Daffodils, tulips and onions develop from bulbs, the bulk of which is made up of fleshy leaf bases. These arise from a small triangular mass of compacted stem and surround the embryo flower shoot.

flowers, such as the wood anemone (*Anemone nemorosa*), the primrose (*Primula vulgaris*) and the lesser celandine (*Ranunculus ficaria*), are in leaf by February and are usually in full bloom by early April. At this time, the tree branches are bare and all the available light is reaching the woodland floor.

Such plants are not strictly woodland inhabitants, however. All tend to grow in open woodlands and on hedge banks, remaining in leaf for much of the summer, but tolerant of shady conditions.

Bulbs and corms

Some other species are more closely geared to the woodland habitat, and are characterized by the special organs that they have developed to store food reserves, their stems having been modified into bulbs and corms. First to flower are the snowdrops (*Galanthus nivalis*),

Above Ramsons (*Allium ursinum*) flower in late spring, after the canopy has partially opened. The pristine white blooms make a pretty display and the plants are instantly recognizable by a strong aroma of onions.

Right The primrose (*Primula vulgaris*) blooms in April. It is not a true plant of woodlands, and is equally common on shady banks and verges, but its leaves are often fully formed by mid-February, in this way beating the trees.

followed by the wild daffodils (*Narcissus pseudonarcissus*), the crocuses (*Crocus*), the bluebells (*Hyacinthoides non-scripta*), and ramsons (*Allium ursinum*).

All produce leaves well before the tree cover becomes detrimental, and these leaves have the sole purpose of stocking the bulb in the ground below with food so that it can produce a flower in the following year. Only the bluebell and ramsons flower after the canopy has closed over. Such plants can be found growing in open fields, but unless they have been planted deliberately and as cultivated hybrids, they often mark the site of an ancient woodland.

What are bulbs and corms? The simplest way to learn about a bulb, without resorting to digging up the garden or the woodlands, is to slice an onion in half from top to bottom. The arrangement revealed is a very short, specialized shoot, consisting of stem and leaf bases that remain permanently underground. At the base, where the straggly roots emerge, is a tough, flattened, slightly triangular area, which is the vegetative stem. From it arise a succession of very swollen leaf bases, the foliage tops of which have withered away. The bulb also contains one or more dormant flowering shoots in the axils of the storage leaves, and around the outside it is protected by brown scaly leaves. In the spring, the shoot will grow through to the soil surface, feeding off the food stored in the leaf bases.

Woodland bulbs are able to develop rapidly in the early spring months because the essential parts of the flowering shoot have already formed underground. Not all the axillary buds formed in the bulb will grow into flowering shoots; some develop into the little offspring bulbils which allow the plants to spread vegetatively underground. The wild daffodil bears a time-honoured association with oak woodlands and, like many of its perennial neighbours, it increases its opportunities for dispersal by producing bulbils as well as seeds. To a similar end, the wood anemone spreads by means of horizontal rootstocks, which serve to disperse new plants through the soil.

Where you see a woodland carpeted with daffodils or bluebells, it is generally an indication that the ground has been undisturbed for a long time, because spread by bulbils is a slow process. The process of carpeting the woodland floor will have been assisted by the spread of seed, but again, there is no rapid result because daffodil seed can take between five and seven years to reach flowering maturity.

Some gardening catalogues will still refer to a crocus corm as a bulb, but a corm has a quite different structure to that of a true bulb. Whereas the bulk of a

Above The snowdrop (*Galanthus nivalis*) is among the first of the spring flowers. The leaves and flowers are able to develop rapidly in the cold weather because the essential parts of the flowering shoot have formed underground during the winter months.

bulb is made up by the fleshy leaf bases, the corm is a highly condensed root-stock – a solid, swollen, underground stem, covered by a thin outer layer of protective scales. If the scales are removed, you will discover the proof that the corm is nothing less than a compacted stem, for it bears scale scars running around its circumference. These are the equivalent of the leaf nodes, and from the nodes near the top sprout the axillary buds that will produce next year's new corms.

If you dig up a crocus in the flowering period, you can see at once that last year's corm is shrivelling up. In fact, it devotes all its food reserves to supplying the flowering shoot and then dies off. One undesirable result of this style of vegetative propagation is that each successive generation tends to grow on top of the preceding year's corms, and this, unless corrected, will result in corms coming ever nearer to the surface. To compensate, the corm produces special roots designed to contract and thus pull the corm down deeper into the soil.

POLLINATION

In spite of such vegetative abilities, all plants rely on proper fertilization from time to time to improve the stock. Woodland flowers still need to produce good pollen and to find pollinators. The problem of living in a woodland environment does not lie entirely with lack of light, but also with fertilization. Pollination, the transfer of male cells or pollen grains from the anthers, where they are produced, to the stigma, which receives them prior to fertilization, is normally effected by one of two agencies: insects or wind. The pollen of a number of aquatic plants, however, is dispersed by water.

Pollinating insects

Many of the pollinating insects, such as bees and butterflies, tend to avoid deeply-shaded areas, even in summer. Being cold-blooded, they are reliant on the warmth of the sun's rays for their metabolism, and prefer to stay out in the open. The fact that most woodland plants flower so early in the year compounds the problem, because few insects are about in any habitats, let alone woodland ones.

The primrose, lesser celandine, daffodil and crocus, in common with almost all early-flowering woodland plants, counter this shortage by producing, in comparison to their size, large eye-catching flowers in bright reflective yellows; flowers designed to lure the few adventuresome pollinators that do emerge on sunny days. Similarly, the wood anemones, snowdrops and ramsons produce showy white flowers. Notice, inciden-

Above All the conifers bear male and female cones in which pollination is effected by wind. The female pine cones take three years to mature and shed ripe seed. This cone is in its third year, after the scales have opened.

tally, how the blooms of the snowdrop, daffodil and bluebell incline their heads downwards; this is a particular adaptation to protect the delicate reproductive organs from spring gales and rainstorms.

Wind pollination

Some, though by no means all, woodland plants are dependent on wind to ensure pollination. These include the conifers and the broad-leaf trees, such as birch (*Betula*), hazel (*Corylus*), willow (*Salix*), alder (*Alnus*), poplar (*Populus*), beech (*Fagus*), and oak (*Quercus*), all of which have flowers arranged in catkins. For a good example of this type of flower, you

Left Hazel (*Corylus*) produces pretty male catkins that hang as golden tassels in the early spring. Their pollen is carried on air currents to the tiny scale-like female flowers. Because the male and female organs are borne in separate inflorescences, the flowers are monoecious.

Right The wood spurge (*Euphorbia amygdaloides*) is a plant of shady places. It grows from a perennial rootstock, and its flowers are greenish, made up of floral leaves, and unisexual, the female being found among many minute single-stamen male flowers. All the spurges exude a milky, acrid juice, which is poisonous.

might pick one of the male catkins of the hazel, easily recognizable by their cylindrical shape. The female organs are borne on a separate, smaller, bud-like catkin, and the flowers are thus *monoecious*. They are to be found from about Christmas until early March, and if you look through a hand lens you will see that the male catkin is made up of tiny flowers, each consisting of a number of green scales enclosing about 8 stamens. There are no petals, and the anthers are exposed to the elements. The female flower is a tiny sessile bud consisting of scales, the vestige of a perianth, and two minute styles connecting with the ovary.

Other trees bear *dioecious* blooms; in other words, the male and female organs are contained within the same flower. Maples (*Acer*) and ash (*Fraxinus*) constitute a half-way advance towards the so-called flowering trees. These include horse chestnut (*Aesculus*), lilac (*Syringa*) and rowan (*Pyrus*), which bear large showy flowers reliant on insects for pollination.

Wind-pollinated flowers can also be found on the woodland floor. Look out for dog's mercury (*Mercurialis perennis*), a member of the spurge family which flowers in spring. Like other wind-pollinated plants, the male and female flowers are separate, with prominent reproductive organs and without obvious petals.

Ensuring cross-pollination

One of the problems for plants with dioecious flowers is the risk of self-pollination. The most frequent method by which cross-pollination is ensured is the maturation of male and female parts at different times. Generally, anthers mature before stigmas, thus necessitating transfer of pollen to an older flower. Less often, the female parts mature first, in which case the pollinating insect has unwittingly to locate a younger flower. When hawthorn (*Crataegus oxycantha*) blossoms, check a flower and you will find that the stigmas and styles are receiving pollen before the anthers of that bloom have developed.

The primrose has evolved an ingenious but delightfully simple way of ensuring cross-pollination, known as *heterostyly*, in which two distinct kinds of flower are borne on separate plants. The so-called pin-eye form has a prominent knob-like stigma on a long style projecting from the mouth of the corolla tube, while the anthers are located half-way down inside.

The thrum-eye primrose adopts the opposite arrangement, with the stamens prominent and the stigma hidden deep in the tube. Successful transfer of pollen, therefore, can only take place between flowers of different types.

WOODLAND HABITATS

There is no such thing as a typical woodland. Certain overall conditions are fairly predictable, but the character will vary according to many factors, and if one is surveying an area of woodland botanically it is important, first, to establish the kind of habitat, irrespective of anything which is growing there. What is the soil type? What is the topography? Is the soil shallow, stony, or with a deep humus layer? And is it a dry or a wet wood? A large wooded tract may include several different conditions which merge into one another, but these things separately will affect the make-up of localized plant communities.

Soil types

The soil type will fall into one of two basic categories: calcareous soil – chalk, limestone and marls, and siliceous soils – clay, loam and sand. Manmade woodlands have, to some extent, broken the natural pattern,

Below Open dry beech woods are often colonized by little more than grasses. On high ground, the soil is usually well drained and the trees remove most of the remaining moisture.

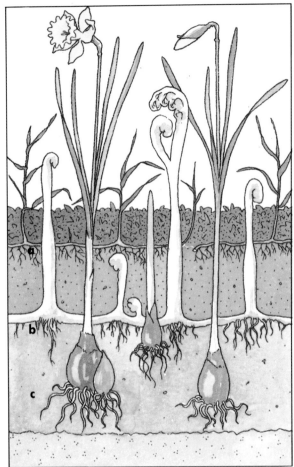

Above Communities of plants complement each other and make the best use of available ground. In an oak wood, the daffodils (**c**) penetrate to the deepest level, their roots reaching the subsoil; bracken rhizomes (**b**) occupy the middle strata of the top soil, and close beneath the leaf litter run the underground stems of the grasses (**a**). The daffodils form leaves and flowers before the bracken starts to emerge.

and one can now find vast plantations growing in untypical positions. In a woodland that has developed naturally, however, the type of soil affects not only the dominant trees that have invaded the area, but also the range of plants making up the undergrowth.

Many tree species will grow on calcareous soils, but certain preferences generally emerge. Calcareous marls, for example, will encourage both oak and ash as dominant trees.

Beech is the typical species on chalk, often accompanied by yew (*Taxus*). Limestones tend to generate a preponderance of ash. On calcareous marshes and fens, alder predominates.

Left In a dry upland oak wood, the trees tend to be small and are distorted by wind action. The soil is often too shallow and impoverished to support larger growths.

Below Hair grass (*Aira flexuosa*) is one of the predominant undergrowth species, colonizing drier upland woods. Its reduced leaves are well adapted to cope with arid conditions.

A similarly varied range of trees is supported by siliceous soils. Lowland clay soils of the kind that retain their moisture encourage oak, but it is predominantly the race which bears sessile leaves (*Quercus pedunculata*). The drier, sandier, and often shallower, soils tend to produce *Q. sessiliflora*. Northern up-lands with siliceous soils also produce birch woods and pine woods. Lowlands support willow and alder.

Dry and wet woods

Notice how, in a typical dry upland oak wood, the trees tend to be smaller and more distorted than their lowland counterparts. This is caused by leaching of nutrients from the stony hilltop, which leads to stunted growth, and by weathering, particularly wind action, which causes twisting and breakage of limbs. The habitat that predominantly supports sessile oak will also include pine, birch, rowan and hawthorn, with an undergrowth of hair grasses (*Aira*), bracken (*Pteridium*), ling (*Calluna*) and bilberry (*Vaccinium*), plants that are generally adapted to cope with drier conditions. It will also host more primitive plants that are capable of withstanding drought and include lichens, mosses and hardier ferns.

In a beech wood set in upland chalk, the undergrowth tends to be even sparser because the trees provide a more dense leaf canopy during summer. Compare the upland scene with a damp lowland wood. The pedunculate oak may be joined by a variety of trees, such as ash, beech, and lime, all of which are common across Europe, and also by species that are of limited native distribution but are now widely spread through introduction. These last include sycamore (*Acer pseudoplatanus*), horse chestnut (*Aesculus hippocastanum*), sweet chestnut (*Castanea sativa*) and hornbeam (*Carpinus betulus*). Beneath the trees, a much wider assortment of herbaceous plants will thrive, as will many more species of ferns and mosses, joined in the very damp and shady parts by liverworts and algae.

NON-FLOWERING PLANTS

A damp woodland is perhaps the best place to gain an acquaintance with the more primitive groups, the non-flowering plants or *cryptogams*, because they tend to be reliant on moisture to a greater extent than the advanced, so-called higher plants, since their simpler members possess no internal water transport system. Such plants were the earliest colonizers of land, and they are still some of the first growths to appear on bare soil or stone. They are also important indicators of air pollution, since few will tolerate the toxic fumes in an urban or industrial atmosphere.

Liverworts

Apart from the algae, which are generally restricted to water, the most primitive green land plants are the liverworts (Hepaticeae) and mosses (Musci). Find a wood with a small stream running through it. Where there are steep earth banks, and exposed rocks or stonework, you may well come across flat spreading cushions of such liverwort species as *Pellia*, *Marchantia* and *Conocephalum*.

Left Butcher's broom (*Ruscus aculeatus*) is not what it seems – its "leaves" are highly modified stem structures which have taken over the function and appearance of leaves. The small flowers develop on the cladodes in the axils of tiny scale leaves.

Above Greater burnet saxifrage (*Pimpinella major*), a member of the Umbelliferae family, is widespread and common on rich soils, often appearing in shady open woodlands. The flowers, clustered in large umbels, may be white or occasionally pink.

There is no distinction between roots, stem and leaves, only a delicate papery thallus which bears anchoring threads underneath, and sometimes possesses a hint of a mid-rib. Other types differentiate into stems and leaves of a kind and are called leafy liverworts, or scale-mosses. For examples of these, look out for *Alicularia* and *Lophozia* species.

In January and February, the liverworts produce tiny sex organs. You will need to search for these with a lens. *Pellia*, one of the commonest, develops special reproductive areas of tissue which produce sex-cells – male *antheridia* near the mid-rib, and female *archegonia* are sited just behind the thallus tip, covered by a form of protective hood. The reproductive cells are *gametes* hence the plant is a *gametophyte*. The male gametes bear tiny hairs, or *cilia*, to enable them to swim

Above One of the commonest members of the liverwort (Hepaticeae) group, | wide nerved liverwort (*Pellia epiphylla*) is wholly dependent on water for its reproduction.

through a film of moisture on the thallus surface and fertilize the female egg cells, hence the necessity for a damp atmosphere. The fertilized cell develops a capsule from which spores will be liberated, and as it matures the capsule is pushed up on a fragile stalk. This is technically another plant, the *sporophyte* which remains wholly dependent on the gametophyte. The capsules can be seen during February and March.

Mosses

Mosses complete a similar life cycle but all are differentiated into stems and leaves, and they are generally less dependent on water. Notice how they can survive in quite dry parts of a woodland, even colonizing tree trunks and exposed rocks, and withstanding prolonged periods of desiccation. Because their leaves have no protective cuticle, their response to drought conditions is to curl up tightly.

Male and female organs appear sometimes on the same, sometimes on separate stems, and develop like tiny flowers with rosettes of leaves. There is a similar swimming necessity for male cells, to enable them to reach their female counterparts, and the sporophyte capsule is again borne on the female stem of the leafy gametophyte plant.

Species of moss may look similar at first glance, but they are a very large group of plants, and constitute a miniature world of fascinating complexity and variety. If you are not familiar with the mosses, some of the larger, more distinctive types like *Atrichum* and *Thuidium* make a good starting point.

Above The pedunculate oak (*Quercus sessiliflora*), one of the commonest native trees of Europe, provides a complete micro-habitat for a wide range | of species, from primitive lichens to mistletoe, with other plants, including some fungi, forming intimate associations with its roots.

Ferns

There is no sensible comparison between the sexual cycle of mosses and liverworts, many of which possess two distinct forms, gametophyte and sporophyte, and of higher plants, whose gametophyte stage has been absorbed totally. In the ferns (Filicales), the two alternating generations separate completely and for the first time the sporophyte stage becomes dominant. If you look on the underside of the leaves of a common type, such as the male fern (*Dryopteris*), you will find sporebearing *sporangia* for much of the year. The liberated spores settle in moist conditions and develop into tiny plants, quite different from the ferns themselves but not unlike thallose liverworts, and these diminutive gametophytes produce the sex cells, which in their turn fuse and develop into new fern plants.

There is still an alternation of distinct generations, but the fern plant, equating to the stalked capsule in mosses and liverworts, is now fully independent of its tiny, fragile, water-dependent alter ego.

If you search the dampest parts of the woodland, particularly on old dead fern "stumps", you should be able to locate the gametophytes, often with minute fern plants developing from them.

Dependent lifestyles

Ferns and mosses frequently use tree trunks and branches as bases from which to grow, and in these circumstances they fall into an ecological category known as *epiphytes*. The term denotes a very gentle and undemanding association between two plants, in which the host is only used for support, and no nourishment is drawn from its tissues. Certain plants have developed an epiphytic habit in order to escape from the intense competition on the woodland floor, and to bring themselves nearer to the source of light.

Because many of the epiphytes are very sensitive to pollution, the best places to find them are in woodlands well away from towns and cities. The most primitive plants, which often live as epiphytes on trees, are the lichens, and they are also widely dispersed on exposed soil and rocks, away from the protective environment of woodlands. They can withstand almost complete drying out for long periods of time, though they still require wet conditions for reproduction. A lichen is not one plant but two, comprising an alga and a fungus, growing together in an intimate arrangement known as *symbiosis*. The fungus usually makes up the bulk of the plant and the microscopic algal cells are buried inside its tissues. The alga manufactures food by photosynthesis and provides the fungus with its source of nourishment. The fungus, in turn, protects the more delicate alga, and in combination the two organisms can inhabit some of the most inhospitable places on earth.

You will find some of the richest assortments of lichens growing on the branches of oaks located on slopes surrounded by pure, crisp, mountain air. The

Above Soft shield fern (*Polystichum setiferum*) grows almost everywhere that there is reasonable shade to be found, though it prefers damp woodlands, often gracing the edges of streams with its elegant foliage.

Right Lichens, a combination of an alga and a fungus, are some of the most primitive forms of plant life and are frequently epiphytic on the branches of trees. They are sensitive indicators of atmospheric pollution.

can be found on a variety of hosts, particularly apple and poplar, though less frequently on the tree with which it is linked by tradition, the oak. The seeds are very often wiped into bark crevices by birds eating the fleshy and very glutinous fruit pulp. They germinate, producing green leaves which photosynthesize normally, but the roots penetrate and fuse with the xylem in the host tissues so that the mistletoe can draw its water and mineral salt requirements from the tree. It is thus a *partial* parasite.

An oak as a micro-habitat

A fascinating botanical study can be made by selecting one large oak tree and examining it as a total environment in order to find out how many different species are being supported, in one way or another, by this single majestic plant. There will perhaps be over half a dozen kinds of lichen growing on the bark, mosses on the lower trunk, and ferns nestling in the crevices of the main branches. You will find very often, incidentally, that the epiphytes growing on a trunk will be somewhat different on its south- and north-facing aspects.

On the older tree, bracket fungi may be invading wounds in the timber. High in the branches, mistletoe may be drawing strength from the oak's sap. In the shade at its foot, plants intolerant of direct sunlight, including enchanter's nightshade (*Circaea*), may be gathered. Other kinds of fungi, such as the death cap (*Amanita phalloides*), may appear to be growing on the soil, but in reality they set up a special interdependent relationship with the oak roots, known as *mycorrhiza*.

Above Some of the ferns are regularly epiphytic on trees, using the trunk for support, but taking no nourishment. Polypodium spreads its tangled rhizomes in the fork of a pollarded ash tree.

Right Inonotus hispidus is one of the most elegant of bracket fungi. The species is parasitic on ash trees, eventually causing considerable damage to the host. It is present all the year round, but new fruiting bodies appear in autumn.

epiphytic mosses, on the other hand, are less able to withstand prolonged drying and therefore tend to be more prolific in areas that enjoy regular rainfall.

Though in no way comparable to the profusion of species in tropical rain forests, a number of ferns grow epiphytically in temperate Europe. One of the commonest and most widespread is *Polypodium*, and if you look at an example you will notice how the interlaced mats of the fern roots, or rhizomes, spread over the boughs of the tree on which the plant is growing, but do not penetrate the bark.

Some plants that grow on trees are dependent on a host-parasite relationship. Mistletoe (*Viscum album*)

CHARTING THE WOOD

Making a scientific record of an overall woodland habitat ideally includes charting the wood. This may seem a bit daunting in principle but it is really quite straightforward and it is the only way to gain an accurate impression of what is going on. Charting reveals the links between the soil, the climatic conditions and the plants growing in the habitat. It will also explain the minor variations that cause the types of plant to vary from one part of the wood to another. In botanical terms, these are *plant associations.*

One, perfectly adequate, way to chart an area of wood is to use a large-scale survey map as a base. This will provide the bird's eye view ground plan from which you can copy the outlines and contour details and use them as a template for your botanical map.

Unfortunately, you may find, if you are trying to include all the relevant details of soil types, dominant tree cover and undergrowth, that you finish up with an unintelligible muddle. The clearest way of charting is to build up a 3-dimensional picture, using a base and then superimposing transparent sheets of the kind used in overhead projectors. You can use as many sheets as necessary to build a complete picture.

Choosing a survey area

The base will bear the contours of the wood, matching those of the survey map, and can include the soil types. Using the same outline, the transparent sheets will then show dominant trees, under-storeys, ground plants, epiphytes and so on. Don't attempt to chart the whole of the wood – that really would be a labour of love. Instead, walk around your area and work out how to take a representative "roadway" through it.

Let us assume, for illustration, that your woodland runs from an escarpment down to a stream valley. Clearly, you will achieve a broader view of the environment if the survey area takes in a strip running from the high ground and into the lowland region. The number of representative sample strips covered by your survey will depend on the extent of variation within the overall ground plan, and the time you have available. You may also find that it is useful to produce a map providing the

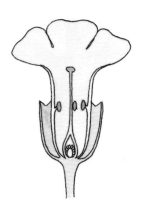 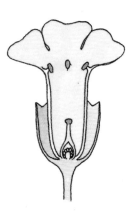

Left A Welsh lowland river wends its way over a granite bed; deciduous woodlands clothe the lower slopes thickly, while above are conifers.

Above Primroses (*Primula vulgaris*) typify a flowering condition known as heterostyly, in which the ingenious arrangement of stamens and pistils effectively prevents self-pollination from the pin-eyed (left) to the thrum-eyed (right) and vice versa.

vertical view, like a slice through a cake, to complement the surface view.

Dominant species

It is essential to distinguish the dominant plants growing in a .particular section. A local preponderance of deciduous larch trees in a section of otherwise evergreen coniferous forest will provide the habitat for a quite different undergrowth to that allowed by spruce or fir, yet without having noted the dominance of larch it will be difficult to account for the variation in patterns. It is equally important to note the position of lone species. The presence of one Scots pine in an oak woodland may have a marked effect on the plants growing within its area of influence. Unless the answers are obvious at a glance, the best approach is to mark out a length of your sample strip – say 30 metres – and count the numbers of trees belonging to each species. Do the same over a reduced area for the undergrowth plants.

One of the fascinations of a survey is to discover changes taking place in the habitat. Of all the tree seeds which fall to the ground – a mature oak tree may produce 30,000 or more acorns every season – very few seedlings survive beyond the first growing season. The majority are eaten by animals, damaged, uprooted, fall prey to disease, or simply do not find the right soil and moisture conditions. In a mixed wood, the seedlings that are growing most vigorously are those best suited to the habitat, and they in their turn may well determine the complexion of that environment in thirty years time.

Above Many woodlands were planted by the landowners of the 18th and 19th centuries as ornamental features of the landscape, and contain exotic species of trees growing far from their native habitats.

Natives and introductions

Having charted the species, the next task is to establish which are naturally endemic to the area, and which have been introduced by man. Here, you must bear in mind that many apparently-natural woodlands were, in fact, planted by the great landowners of the 18th and 19th centuries as extensions to the more formal parts of their estates.

You may well discover trees and herbaceous plants that are essentially foreign. By way of illustration, the sweet Spanish chestnut (*Castanea*) has been naturalized all over temperate Europe because of the popularity of its edible fruits. The red oak (*Q. rubra*) was introduced from America for its timber. The walnut (*Juglans*) came from South-east Asia for the combined value of its fruits and its pretty wood. Sometimes the history of a species comes as a surprise: for example, a person living in the British Isles or France might be excused for imagining that the sycamore was a native tree, but this is not so. Originally, it was limited to central Europe. As the oaks were cut out of the forests, however, sycamores were often planted in their place because they are, by comparison, more rapid growers, and once a single specimen becomes established it will quickly spread itself by particularly robust self-sown seedlings.

HOW OLD ARE THE TREES?

It is difficult to calculate the age of a living tree any other way than by rule of thumb because you cannot chop it in half to inspect its growth rings. A mature beech in a protected environment can live to between 100 and 200 years, and some surviving oaks are probably double that age. Unless uprooted by gales or massively attacked by disease, as in the case of the Dutch elm epidemic, the death of a tree is a slow process. Little by little, it is invaded and weakened.

Most mature trees increase in girth by between 2 and 3cm each growing season, although this figure can vary – a slow-growing species, such as yew, will put on far less girth, while a sycamore, by contrast, will expand more rapidly. Some of the oldest oaks have reached a circumference of more than 20 metres! Trees grow up

Below A mature oak (*Quercus robur*) is often 200 years old, and can attain a girth of more than 20 metres. One of the biggest of the broad-leaved trees, it can reach a height of 40 metres, growing at a rate of some 30cm a year, but slowing as it matures.

Left Trees do not live forever. Eventually, like all other living things, they succumb to disease and old age. Most woodlands are managed, old and dangerous timber being felled and removed.

Right Coppicing changes the appearance of a woodland dramatically. Traditionally, hazel (*Corylus*) was frequently coppiced, the main trunk being cut regularly at ground level, to produce a profusion of stems which were valuable as fencing poles and stakes.

to 30cm a year by elongation, though the rate slows as they become older. The biggest broad-leaf trees – oak, beech, and elm – can mature to a height of over 40 metres. Ash is generally slightly smaller, at about 30 metres, with such species as sycamore and horse chestnut achieving about 20 metres.

Coppicing and pollarding

Very few so-called "natural" woodlands have not, at one time or another, felt the hand of man to manage them. Trees become overcrowded, diseased and dangerous in old age, and since earliest times thinning and tree surgery have been established practices for keeping a woodland healthy.

There are several techniques that dramatically change the natural appearance of trees. Coppicing, for the production of fencing poles and stakes, has been carried out extensively over past centuries. On certain trees, particularly hazel, the main trunk is cut regularly at ground level at five-year intervals, creating a stump or "stool". The surgery encourages large numbers of long straight stems to grow out in clusters. Traditionally, hazels have been grown together with oak and ash, the larger trees rendering timber, and the hazel producing a constant supply of poles, thus making the most profitable use of the available ground.

Pollarding generates a similar effect on the tree, but in this case the main trunk is cut at a height above which grazing animals cannot reach to browse on the tender, newly-emerged shoots. The trees most frequently pollarded are willows, producing long supple wands, used in basket-making.

Calculating the height

There is a convenient and very simple method of calculating the height of a tree without climbing to the top and dangling a tape measure. Assuming that the average person has a reach of about 60cm, take an ordinary 30cm rule, or cut a stick of similar length. Holding it vertically at arm's length, walk away from the tree you wish to measure, until the top and bottom of the stick line up with the base and crown of the tree. Mark the spot for safety and pace out the distance back to the tree. The length of a stride varies, but most people take steps that are roughly ½m in length. Halve the measured distance to the tree, and the figure you finish up with is the tree height.

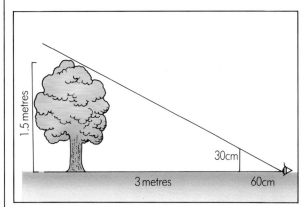

Above Calculating the height of a tree is easy and does not involve dangling a tape measure from the top! All you need is a piece of stick, and a head for simple mathematics. In the example above, the tree is approximately 1.5 metres.

TREES IN WINTER

The best time to study the architecture of a deciduous tree is in the winter when the branches are bare. In a temperate climate, the colder months are unsuitable for active growth, and so the leaves are shed in order to protect the plant. A tree is essentially a form of plant growth which develops as a single, massive, woody stem supporting main branches which divide again and again, resulting in the typical profile. As the tree matures, the yearly extension growth becomes progressively less. Furthermore, once the stem starts to thicken, it can no longer put on lengthwise growth because the cells responsible for this are located just behind the growing apex. The result is that a branch which emerges just a metre from ground level on a young sapling will still be at the same height when the tree is 100 years old.

You should be able to distinguish the commoner tree types in winter by the overall shape, the appearance of the dormant buds, and the features of the bark. Each tree species develops its own identifying features, although external factors such as wind action can strongly affect the appearance. It is often easy to work out the direction of the prevailing wind by looking at the way a tree has grown and weathered: on an exposed site, the ends of the boughs will be swept over towards the lee side.

Get to know the shape, colour, and arrangement of buds. Drawing aspects of winter trees is the surest way of learning about them. Amongst broad-leaf trees, the thick sticky buds of horse chestnut, the hard black ones of ash, and the fine spindle-shaped tips of beech are very easy to recognize and make a useful starting point.

Below The leaves of horse chestnut (*Aesculus hippocastanum*) unfurl in spring from fat bud scales covered in a sticky resin. These protect the telescoped shoot from the frost and gales of winter.

Above Learn to distinguish winter twigs by examining the features of the buds and bark. Ash (*Fraxinus*) bears distinctively black and triangular-shaped buds, which arise from a greyish-brown background.

Bark and bark rubbings

In addition to distinctive buds, different species can be identified by their bark. The trunks of horse chestnut and beech are smooth in the young trees, but the former cracks into small irregular patterns as the tree ages, whereas beech remains smoothly granular throughout life, often retaining a pallid bloom. Ash, by contrast, though again smooth in the sapling, becomes deeply sculptured into lengthwise cracks and crevices as it matures. Conifers too, possess characteristic barks. Pine, larch, and yew have flaky bark which comes away in patches as the trunk expands. Spruce bark, by contrast, is more continuous but slightly warty.

It is more difficult to draw bark, but bark rubbing is a very easy compromise and creates an accurate record

without one needing to be an accomplished artist.

You will require some sheets of strong paper that will not tear or perforate when rubbed on a rough surface, and charcoal drawing sticks or a thick wax crayon. Pin the paper to the bark and rub the "flat" of the drawing stick over the surface lightly until the impression appears. A degree of skill is needed to achieve just the right pressure but perseverence pays off. Spray the rubbing with fixative to avoid smudging.

Seasonal changes

Observing trees is a round-the-year pleasure; as the spring advances, watch how the buds swell and unfold. Sketches of the opened leaves will complete the tree record, but you may also choose to collect representative leaves and press them. (See "Drying and preserving" on p 34 for details.)

As winter approaches, the chemical changes that

Above The trunk of ash (*Fraxinus*) is clothed with bark that is smooth in young growth, but becomes deeply fissured into lengthwise cracks and crevices as it matures.

Right The tree uses its leaves as a waste dump for the by-products of its metabolism. As the green chlorophyll is reabsorbed in autumn, these combine with other pigments, altering the colour balance towards yellow, red, and purple.

take place in the leaves result in the brilliant burst of autumn colour. Chlorophyll is the dominant pigment in green leaves, but they also contain several others, including carotenoids (yellows and orangey reds), anthoxanthins (deep reds and purples), and xanthophylls (yellows). The yellow and russet hues result from a re-absorption of chlorophyll, which leaves the balance altered in favour of the yellow, red, and purple pigments. The tree also uses its leaves as a waste dump and, prior to abscission, toxic materials are transported into the leaf tissues. Not all deciduous trees shed their dead leaves at once though. Notice how young beech will retain its withered leaves through much of the winter.

DEFORESTATION AND RECOLONIZATION

From time to time, major changes occur in a woodland plant community. Trees are felled *en masse* for timber or clearance, and nature also takes her toll. Forest fires cause enormous periodic destruction, and violent autumn storms, if they strike while the trees are still in leaf, can bring them down with equal ferocity. Following such a holocaust, a fascinating time awaits practical botanists, because changes to the environment that are so radical are bound to result in a new kind of flora. The process is known as recolonization.

The recolonizers

If the ground has been completely denuded as a result of burning, some of the first plants to recolonize are mosses. All the early colonizers are types that spread by microscopic spores wafted in on air currents. Before the mosses appear, blue-green algae form slimy patches on the cinders and ash, and they help to create a suitable medium for the growth of larger species. Some cup fungi (*Peziza*) are specially geared to grow on ash and cinders. Fire moss (*Funaria hygrometrica*) will form a bright green carpet in the first season following a fire, spreading over charred soil.

If the habitat is damp, the crescent cup liverwort (*Lunularia cruciata*) is one of the first of the Hepaticeae to appear on cinders. *Lunularia* is native to the Mediterranean region but has been spread throughout Europe as a casual introduction with pot plants and is thus very often found in gardens along a cinder pathway or in a greenhouse. The plant spreads by special vegetative "buds", called gemmae. These develop in the crescent-shaped cups on the upper

Above Gales wreak their own selection process on woodlands, culling out the weaker and older trees, though storm damage can frequently destroy healthy trees through a "domino" effect.

Left Ground that has been laid bare will be recolonized in a very precise sequence, starting with the most primitive plant forms and continuing until trees become re-established.

surface of the thallus and are washed out in raindrops. Amongst the ferns, bracken (*Pteridium aquilinum*) is one of the earliest to recolonize.

Following the more primitive Cryptogams, a number of opportunist higher plants appear. Notice how many of these early colonizers have light seeds with special modifications to blow them in on the air currents. Willowherb seeds are borne on long feathery styles. Thistle seeds develop feathery hairs, as do those of dandelions. Others, most notably bramble (*Rubus fructicosus*), are spread rapidly by animals. Some are adapted to cope specifically with the conditions on burnt ground. Fire weed, or rosebay willowherb (*Epilobium angustifolium*), is one of the most successful. Others, including heather species, bear a remarkable ability to recover after burning down to their roots. Once these pioneers have established themselves, grasses and tree seedlings of birch, rowan, hazel and alder will make a speedy appearance, carried in on the feet and in the droppings of birds and animals.

Burnt or denuded stumps also offer a focal point for recolonization, providing a firm base, organic food material and shelter. In areas of woodland which have been felled, these are often the first places to show signs of new plant growth.

For a time the original flora may continue to grow, but gradually the true woodland plants will lose ground against the competition of hardier species used to surviving in open conditions.

Above left Often, old stumps form a localized area of shelter and provide a focus for recolonization, offering a firm platform and a source of organic food.

Above right Certain fungi, including the cup fungus *Peziza petersii*, will quickly invade bonfire sites. This species appears on burnt soil in late summer and autumn.

Above The brilliant flowers of rosebay willowherb (*Epilobium angustifolium*) often form dense patches, evidencing soil that has witnessed fire. The species is also known as "fireweed", and appeared in profusion on bomb sites during World War II.

FUNGI

The most specialized group of woodland plants, and one which generally needs to be considered separately because its members are so different from any of the other flora, are the fungi.

These are ancient but extraordinarily successful forms which live either as parasites on living trees and other plants, or as saprophytes drawing their nourishment from dead and dying plant rubbish. For this reason, they possess no chlorophyll and do not need light for growth, but on the other hand, they are dependent on a ready and constant supply of organic food material. They also require damp shady conditions because, like other primitive plants, many are particularly vulnerable to drying out.

The higher fungi, which have large fruiting bodies and grow in woods and fields, need particular conditions of humidity and temperature to appear. The damp, cool autumn conditions suit most fungi, though some appear in spring, some in summer, and a few throughout the year. The fungus body which you find growing on the soil or emerging from tree bark is only what might be called the fruit of the plant, correctly known as the *sporophore*. The vegetative body, the equivalent of roots, stem, and leaves, takes the form of a loose mesh of colourless threads called *hyphae* which collectively form a *mycelium*. This vegetative body exists permanently hidden below the surface of soil or bark. If you find a fruiting body growing on the woodland floor and you carefully scrape away the leaf litter, you will unearth the mycelium, which looks like a scattering of teased-out cotton-wool.

Many fungi are host-specific, and will only grow when in association with a particular species of tree. Hence the common Jew's ear fungus (*Auricularia auricula*), which can be found all year round, only appears on elder (*Sambucus*). Likewise the birch bracket (*Piptoporus betulinus*) is restricted to dying birch trees.

Some of the parasitic species are highly destructive and cause great economic damage in plantations. The bracket fungus *Heterobasidium* is a major problem in conifer plantations and is responsible for the deaths of many timber-producing trees each year. The bootlace fungus (*Armillaria mellea*) is also a major pest in a wide variety of trees, attacking the heartwood. Old infected stumps often produce huge numbers of the fruiting bodies in autumn.

Above Most fungi that grow directly on trees are host-specific. The so-called Jew's ear fungus (*Auricularia auricula*) is limited wholly to elder (*Sambucus nigra*).

Left The bootlace or honey fungus (*Armillaria mellea*) causes enormous economic damage to a wide variety of trees, attacking the heartwood with its thick, penetrating, "bootlace" strands of mycelia.

Right The birch bracket (*Piptoporus betulinus*) grows only on birch trees, and once it has gained a hold, the host is doomed. The fungus penetrates through the woody tissues, dissolving and absorbing them as nourishment. Such fungi are strict parasites and saprophytes.

MEADOWS, PASTURES AND CORNFIELDS
INTRODUCTION

If most of Europe was originally covered by forest, today the greater part is dominated by pasture, which extends from water meadows to grassy mountain slopes. Wetlands and mountain pastures will be considered later; in this chapter we are looking at the typical lowland fields.

Pastures and meadows are essentially grasslands, the chief difference being that pastures are fairly natural environments in the sense that they comprise wild grass species grazed casually by flocks and herds, while meadows are more deliberately cultivated and managed. Meadow grasses are, in effect, selected and grown as a cash crop to be mown for hay or silage. These days they generally comprise lush, rapidly-growing species introduced by man. Furthermore, meadows experience crop rotation. Traditionally, they yield a grass crop one year; they are under arable cultivation the next, and lie fallow the third, although the use of modern fertilizers has tended to dispense with this precise cycle. Cornfields are utilized to grow annual cereal crops and are ploughed up in the autumn either to be left fallow over winter or sown with winter germinating varieties.

Regional variations

Most grasses are perennial and together they form one of the largest families of flowering plants. The types of grass vary according to conditions. It is important, firstly, to distinguish between grasses (Graminae) and sedges (Cyperaceae): grasses have round stems, hollow except at the nodes, and the stems bear alternate leaves arranged in two opposite series; sedge stems, in contrast, are triangular and are often filled with spongy tissue.

In a soil with a more or less neutral pH, which constitutes the majority of lowland pastures and

Below Flower meadows are a rarity in many parts of Europe, where they have been destroyed by aggressive application of herbicides and by the introduction of thick, luxuriant grass strains, which effectively smother the more delicate flowering species.

meadows, the dominant species include perennial rye grass (*Lolium perenne*), meadow grass (*Poa pratensis*), Timothy grass (*Phleum pratense*), meadow foxfoot (*Alopecurus pratensis*) and cocksfoot (*Dactylis glomerata*).

The British Isles is one of the best European growing areas for grasses because of its damp warm Atlantic weather, and many varieties currently grown in continental meadows have their origin in British grass seed. For example, Italian rye grass (*Lolium multiflorum*) is almost certainly a larger and more lush cultivar of English-produced *L. perenne* seed.

On sandy or gravelly soils, with good drainage but generally of acidic pH, you will find a predominance of fescues, including sheep's fescue (*Festuca ovina*), of which there are several varieties, the most common across Europe probably being red fescue (*F. rubra*). Where the ground is more waterlogged, meadow fescue (*F. elatior*), in company with the silky agrostis (*Agrostis spica-venti*), may often predominate. Alkaline chalk soils with good drainage most frequently support sheep's fescue.

The list is, of course, a generalization. Individual regions vary considerably in the species of grass to be found there. Grasses are very much a specialized subject because of the number of species and varieties, many of which do not have obvious distinguishing characteristics by which the beginner may separate them. It is best to concentrate on getting to know the dominant species in one area rather than trying to learn grass recognition as a whole.

Above Lowland meadows lying beside rivers are often subject to flooding in spring and autumn. In the Wye valley soils rich in nutrients result in an abundance of wild flowers where the meadows have not been chemically treated.

Below The cornflower (*Centaurea cyanus*) is now a rarity growing wild in cornfields, the victim of herbicides. Its garden counterpart is a broader leaved variety but the flowers are the same brilliant blue.

GRASS INFLORESCENCE

The individual flowers of all grasses are built on the same basic plan, but the way the inflorescence is assembled varies. Grasses are wind pollinated, and the flowers are typically small and will need to be inspected under a magnifying lens, and perhaps teased apart with a needle. They are arranged in *spikelets*, either stalked or sessile, which are grouped into compound *spikes* or into *panicles*.

A spike is a main flowering axis, which becomes elongated and on which sessile flowers are arranged, looking as if they were congregated in a tightly packed cylinder. Typical examples of this are to be found in species such as perennial rye grass (*Lolium*) or wheat (*Triticum*). A spikelet is merely a diminutive spike stemming from the main axis.

A panicle differs from a spike in that the flowers are borne on stalks arising from the main axis. If the stalks are long the panicle is loose, as in oat (*Avena sativa*). If they are short it is dense, as in Timothy grass.

A grass flower

In a typical grass flower, the petals and sepals are absent, and the reproductive organs are enclosed in a pair of protective bracts called *pales*. Each spikelet includes one, two or three flowers, and the spikelet itself is enclosed within two more bracts called *glumes*. The flower proper consists of a simple ovary with two feathery stigmas, designed to catch the minute pollen grains being carried on the breezes.

At the base of the ovary are two minute scales called *lodicules* which, according to some theories, are all that remain of the petals and sepals. Typically, there are three stamens (sometimes two), their anthers borne on long slender filaments.

Grasses may have markedly differing appearances, not only from species to species but according to whether the flowers of an individual plant are in bud, in flower or in fruit. The inflorescence of a grass undergoes considerable change between budding and flowering because the lodicules force the pales apart as they swell. At the same time the filaments of the stamens elongate and the anthers hang out of the

Below left The dwarf grass *Aegelops* grows extensively around the Mediterranean regions and is thought to be the forerunner of modern wheat.

Right Grass inflorescences are unlike those of any other flowering plant being highly modified for effective dispersal. Each flower is minute, lacking petals and sepals, and is protected by scaly bracts.

Below right Cocksfoot (*Dactylis glomerata*) is among the commonest and most distinctive of grasses flowering from spring onwards. Coarse and stiff it grows to 60cm and has dense clusters of spikelets.

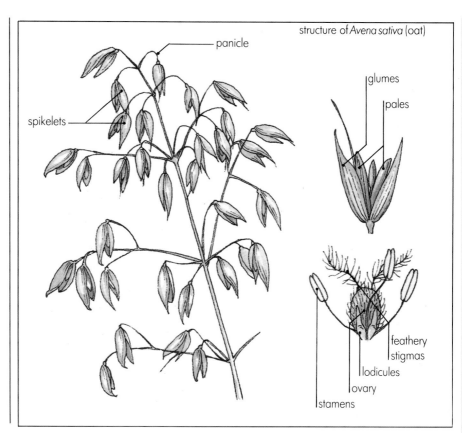

structure of *Avena sativa* (oat)

panicle

spikelets

glumes

pales

feathery stigmas

lodicules

ovary

stamens

flower. It is sometimes difficult for a beginner to appreciate that Gramineae, like any other group of flowering plants, have budding and opening stages.

Rhizomes

The real secret of the success of grasses in dominating open ground lies in their means of spread. Apart from seeding, all grasses propagate by means of special underground stems or *rhizomes*.

There is no need to dig up someone's pasture to explore the efficiency of this mechanism. If you have any couch grass, *Elymus* (*Agropyron*) *repens* growing uninvited in a flower bed, it provides a powerful illustration. Dig some out and you will find that slender but tough rhizomes can extend a considerable distance through the soil, putting up erect stems as they go. If the couch grass has become established, the rhizomes form a thick interlacing mat.

Not only does this provide for very rapid spread through the soil, it effectively prevents less robust plants from getting a roothold.

CLOSED AND OPEN COMMUNITIES

It is important to realize that a pasture or meadow is a *closed community*. The term is a scientific one, meaning that the ground is saturated with plants. They fill the air space above soil surface, and their roots occupy all the available area below ground. The area is consequently unlikely to undergo rapid change, because there are no unoccupied spaces.

If the ground is ploughed, however, as will be the case with a cornfield or a young meadow, the area instantly becomes an *open community*. It does not undergo a succession of changes in the sense that a burnt habitat becomes recolonized from nothing; the effect of ploughing is less severe, and the growth of many plants is disrupted only temporarily, but in that breathing space opportunist species are able to establish themselves in the open soil. Carefully watch the dominant plants which emerge on turned ground – the species will include many which were not apparent in the closed, well established pasture or meadow.

Typically, you will find such buccaneering species as red poppies (*Papaver rhoeas*), groundsel (*Senecio vulgaris*), white goosefoot (*Chenopodium album*) and chickweed (*Stellaria media*). If you are able to compare the list over subsequent years, you will note that these short-term dominants are gradually forced out

and, providing that the habitat is grazed, it will return to the more stable plant associations that it had before. Chickweed may reappear, forming in places where cattle have trampled.

The character of a grassland

Plant associations are perhaps most obvious in a grassland habitat. Remember, whenever you are studying a habitat, that plants rarely grow in isolation; certain species tend to be associated with other plants and will have features in common. In any area, one or two plant species will dominate the rest, their superior numbers being dictated by soil type, water table, altitude, degree of exposure and, directly or indirectly, by man, who will have introduced alien species, applied agrochemicals, ploughed, and perhaps altered patterns of grazing.

Grazing and mowing are the single most important

Above Chickweed (*Stellaria media*) is an opportunist weed of grasslands, quickly establishing itself wherever its seeds land on bare or disturbed soil. In time, it is gradually forced out by more permanent species.

Left Of all the annuals that invade meadows and cornfields, the red field poppy (*Papaver rhoeas*) must be one of the prettiest. However, its brilliant flowers are ephemeral; they bloom, are pollinated, and then fertilized in just a single day.

Above Pastures differ from meadows and cornfields in being the least managed kind of grassland. The closed community of a pasture is rarely disturbed, and often it is grazed only by sheep and cattle. In the main, pastures support perennial species of wildflower.

Below Grassland perennials are often characterized by extensively spreading rooting systems. The creeping buttercup (*Ranunculus repens*) is aptly named, because it propagates over a wide area by means of underground stems.

annuals, while cornfields include mainly annuals. Furthermore, a pasture, which may never have seen a plough, theoretically sustains a much greater variety of flowers and grass species than a meadow or cornfield.

Perennials

Perennials that commonly thrive in permanent pastures have to be able to compete with the super-efficient propagation techniques of the grasses. Some benefit from similar creeping underground stems; these include such species as the creeping buttercup (*Ranunculus repens*) and rest harrow (*Ononis arvensis*). Others which possess vigorous abilities to spread are field crowfoot (*Ranunculus acris*), bulbous

factors influencing the stability of a grassland, and without these regulators it would be an ephemeral habitat. It is not only domestic animals that graze, but also wild herbivores, such as rabbits. Without the influence of four-legged lawn-mowers, most grasslands will slowly change to scrub and finally to woodland. When the first major outbreak of myxomatosis hit the rabbit population in Europe, the enormous decline in rabbit numbers dramatically altered many habitats on which the advance of scrub vegetation had previously been suppressed. Mowing by manmade machinery produces similar results, but the effect varies according to the regularity and severity of the cut.

For the botanist, a distinction between pastures and cornfields is that the former include predominantly perennial species of wild flower, with a few intrusive

Above Like the creeping buttercup, rest harrow (*Ononis arvensis*) has a robust ability to spread through a grassland by means of underground stems.

Below The curled dock (*Rumex crispus*), a member of the dock and sorrel family, possesses tough woody rootstocks that resist removal and will quickly sprout again from mown stumps.

field scabious (*Scabiosa arvensis*). Some, like tormentil (*Potentilla erecta*), possess tough woody rootstocks; others, such as dock (*Rumex*), hogweed (*Heracleum*) and thistles (*Carduus*), have deep tap roots.

Such perennials have to do battle successfully on several fronts. Modern farming demands that weeds are regularly mown off and it is only the more tenacious species, such as thistles, docks and hogweeds, which develop deep rooting systems, that survive this, and

buttercup (*R. bulbosus*), daisy (*Bellis perennis*) and these also tend to flower and produce seed quite rapidly. The same plants also have to compete with the agrochemical weapons that man throws at them. Changes in management practice, and the use of selective hormonal weedkillers which tend to over-stimulate and kill off Dicotyledones but not Monocotyledones, to which the grasses belong, have now turned many grasslands into sterile acres in which only some of the hardier so-called weeds can survive.

Meadow plants

Meadows, too, have changed substantially. Because spring haymaking has been made possible through the development of new and vigorous strains of grasses, those wild flowers which manage to grow tend to be cut down before they have an opportunity to spread seed, even more severely than in pastures. Furthermore, the types of grass species are controlled, and the seed is screened to eliminate weeds. Once, meadows comprised a hotch-potch of grass varieties, typically with fine leaves and slender flowering stems which were shorter than those of modern hybrids. Modern grass hybrids are bred genetically to produce thick luxuriant growth, which may be ideal for high hay yields, but which effectively stifles many low-growing grassland flowers. The seed is also pure in content, being screened to eliminate stray seeds of other plants.

In consequence, most of the more delicate meadow flowers have all but disappeared in areas of Europe that are intensively managed. Sometimes, one can come across an ancient flower meadow on some derelict farm estate, perhaps untouched by chemicals and cropped only by sheep, where a riot of grassland flowers still thrive – cowslips (*Primula veris*) in the spring, followed by cuckoo flower (*Cardamine pratensis*), orchids, and a host of blooms such as the pimpernel (*Anagallis*), the corn marigold (*Chrysanthemum segetum*) and the cornflag (*Gladiolus segetum*). Where agriculture is less intense, such sights are more common, and in some of the poorer farming areas of southern Europe, the spring meadows are still carpeted with blooms which include beautiful species like the anemones (*A. pavonina*) and (*A. coronaria*).

Cornfields

Likewise, cornfields that once harboured a variety of lovely flowers scattered in amongst cereal crops like wheat and barley are now frequently barren places. In the past, the seed that was sown included many annual meadow flower species, such as sow thistle (*Sonchus*

Left Sadly most flower meadows have been "sprayed away" and replanted with cultivar grasses.

Below Lady's smock (*Cardamine pratensis*) is so called because when the flowers are massed they look like washing laid out to dry, by the old country method, on the meadow grass. Notice how the flowers are borne on long stalks to compete with spring grasses.

oleraceus), corn forget-me-not (*Myosotis arvensis*) and shepherd's purse (*Capsella bursa-pastoris*), because farmers were unable to separate these out.

Commercial seed production is now so rigorously managed that these and species such as the cornflower (*Centaurea cyanus*) and the fumitory (*Fumaria officinalis*) are almost extinct across large areas of Europe. They, too, are attacked by herbicides, and eliminated by modern methods of seed screening. Some hardy opportunists, such as poppies and mayweeds, manage to survive because their seeds can lie dormant in the soil for long periods. The poppy is also particularly adapted for a life which is, in effect, an annual race with the reaper. Its flowers open and are pollinated in a single day and the poppy seed is "set" very rapidly. You will find no nectaries in a poppy flower; instead, it relies on hidden ultra-violet coloration to lure pollinating insects with an unmistakable message. But the poppy and the other aggressive annuals are exceptional, and more fragile annual plants need to be re-sown with the cereal seeds each year if they are to make an appearance.

Modern cereal crops provide peculiar conditions, akin to a miniature woodland plantation. The varieties are genetically engineered to grow rapidly, with thick foliage that will pump nourishment into the massive seed heads. The result, ecologically, is very obvious if you get down on your hands and knees and peer between the rows of mature plants in a wheatfield. Bare stalks rise for 20cm or so and then sprout a thick canopy of leaves. The effect is to generate a gloomy, barren, desert beneath.

MAKING A SURVEY

True flower meadows and pastures are worthy of protection for the future, and in some European countries there is now a mechanism that permits them to be turned into nature reserves.

For an individual to achieve such ends is by no means impossible, but it does require a lot of hard work and determination, often against heavy opposition from agricultural consortiums which may wish to take over and exploit under-used areas for commercial gain. On the other hand, what more delightful way could there be of spending a fine early summer's day, than sitting amidst the sights and sounds of a flower meadow, drawing or painting?

It is important to make a careful analysis, not only of the plants growing in the area of grassland on which you have decided to concentrate, but of the various influences brought to bear on them. As with the woodland, you will need to identify all the species, and then list them in order of dominance, beginning with a grouping of those which predominate, then those which are moderately frequent, and finally the occasionals and rarities.

How does one effectively survey a pasture or meadow, though, when perhaps it extends over ten hectares or more? Quite obviously, you cannot spend days and weeks covering every inch of the ground! The technique is to take one or more representative samples, a kind of "straw poll".

A quadrat frame

Make a square frame, which can be constructed out of anything from haberdashery tape to plywood, with a side length of one metre. If the material used is solid, you may want to hinge the frame so that you can carry it folded or flattened. The device is properly called a *quadrat frame*. Throw the square on the ground more or less at random – within the frame is your area of operation, and this will provide a fairly reliable means of assessment. Check over the metre area carefully and list all the species that you find.

You will probably be astonished by the number of different species of plant that are growing there. It may not be possible to identify everything straight away, but don't worry. Collect samples of anything which appears unfamiliar, so that you can examine them on the kitchen table at your leisure, but beware of contravening either local or national conservation laws!

Left Charting a grassland is best done with a quadrat frame. This one was made very cheaply from lengths of plastic curtain rail and some white binding tape.

Charting the area

The next stage is to draw up a quadrat chart. Take a large piece of paper (A4 or bigger) and mark out a scaled-down square. Unless there are obvious demarcations of grass species, they will be spread fairly evenly. Nonetheless, note the types growing within the quadrat area. Then note the location of the various other species. Finally, count the numbers of plants of each species growing within the square and record them against a check-list. The record should be dated and identified with an appropriate location, such as a map grid-reference. By making several quadrat charts over the appropriate areas of the grassland habitat you should then be able to build up an overall ground plan. If there are obvious variations of plant association within the meadow – for example, if one end is boggy and the other is on a dry, windswept slope – you will need to take samplings in both types of habitat. By the same token, if one side is shaded by large trees for most of the day, and the other is exposed, these will need to be compared and contrasted.

Above An upland pasture may well offer more than one habitat, running down from a well-drained height to a boggy water meadow. All must be taken into consideration.

If the area slopes, running from a high, well-drained point down into a valley, it may also be very useful to build up a transect map, slicing through as for the woodland. This will more readily show the changes in vegetation in relation to the land contours.

As with the woodland, the result may also be less muddled if you have a base chart of the meadow or pasture, with grasses and flowers superimposed separately on transparent sheets.

Avoid the temptation of sampling close to a hedge or field boundary though, unless you also note the fact that the vegetation may not be representative of the rest of the area. A meadow containing a comparatively small number of species over the majority of its surface may sport a deceptively wide variety at the edges because the conditions are not typically those of a true grassland.

PLANT ASSOCIATIONS

Within a grassland association some of the plants will, to a degree, relate to one another in terms of growth and flowering periods. For illustration, red poppies (*Papaver rhoeas*) and scentless mayweed (*Matricaria inodora*) are both opportunist annuals which invariably grow together and flower simultaneously. Others will relate in terms of rooting depth, or in the height of their flowering shoots. In particular, they will be influenced by the dominant grasses in amongst which they must grow, be successfully pollinated, and produce seed.

If you imagine this last factor to be an irrelevance, consider that in a meadow, chickweed (*Stellaria media*), a weak straggling annual that never reaches more than a few centimetres from ground level, will often reach its peak of growing and flowering in winter, when the grass is very short.

The cowslip, which flowers and has its strongest growth period in the spring, when the grasses are just beginning to elongate, relies on a flat rosette of leaves and a fairly short flowering stalk. These attributes are ideal for a plant that has no problem of competition for light but has to cope with spring gales. They would, on the other hand, be useless for a species like the corn cockle (*Lychnis githago*), which grows up and flowers with the grasses. The corn cockle develops tall stems with leaves arranged along their length, and elongated flower stalks to push the flowers up to a level with the grass tops. All of these things tell their own story and should be carefully noted.

Animals will also graze selectively, affecting the make-up of plant associations. Daffodils may be growing in a spring pasture – indication that it was once a woodland – but while sheep and cattle will browse all around, certain repellent chemicals produced in the leaves will prevent the daffodils being grazed. Other plants, like thistles, are armoured with spines, making them physically unpalatable.

Natives and introductions

One of the most important aspects of your survey will be to establish which plants grow naturally in the habitat, and which have been introduced by man. A good, comprehensive flora of your country, as distinct from an ordinary illustrated field guide, will identify the probable origin of a species and its introduced range.

Adjacent to cultivated ground where cereal and hay hybrids are grown regularly, wind and accidental

Above The scentless mayweed (*Matricaria inodora*) typically grows in close proximity to the red poppy and flowers simultaneously with it, forming a true grassland association.

Right In areas of grassland that are not subject to heavy trampling, species of thistle, including *Carduus lanceolatus*, grow tall, relying on their defensive armoury of prickles to keep would-be browsers at bay.

scattering will increase the proportion of aliens, particularly on the leeward side. Historically, many of the flowers of cereal crops have been spread casually with the harvested seed. Fumitory is, by origin, a plant of the Mediterranean regions, but over the centuries it was dispersed throughout the cultivated area of Europe.

Sometimes more subtle historical links will emerge. Alongside ancient trackways on upland meadows in the south-east of England, one can occasionally find field fleawort (*Senecio integrifolius*), which is generally of upland continental distribution but was almost certainly introduced to England on the feet of Roman legionaries. Another species, *Senecio paludosus*,

Left By contrast, the dwarf thistle (*Carduus acaulis*) thrives on pathways because it has adopted a rosette habit, its leaves flat to the ground and its flowers arising from very short stalks.

which is limited to a few fenland spots in eastern England and the Channel Islands, was similarly brought across the English channel by immigrants and invaders.

The scarcity of a particular species is not always due to man's interference. A plant may have become established, through introduction, on the limits of its climatic range. The bee orchid (*Ophrys apifera*) is essentially a flower of dry limestone pastures in central and southern Europe occurring no further north than central Germany. It may appear occasionally in areas above these latitudes, however, where its scarcity is due to inclement temperatures rather than loss of suitable habitat.

Trampling

Notice other effects of man and animals on a grassland. A footpath across a field will support a different flora compared with that of the surrounding area. Two factors will have come into play: the effect of treading will have eliminated plants with tall stems which would be damaged by such activity, but it will not have affected the tougher low-growing species with flat rosettes of leaves; this in turn will provide more light at ground level, promoting the low-growers still further.

Thistles provide a good illustration of this effect. The common spear thistle (*Carduus lanceolatus*), with stems up to 150cm tall, may be growing freely in a pasture, but on the pathway it will be absent in favour of the dwarf thistle (*C. acaulis*), which is distinguished by the almost total absence of a stem.

HEDGES, VERGES AND SCRUBLAND
INTRODUCTION

One of the most productive areas for the practical botanist is scrub: land which was once pasture or woodland and which now represents a half-way stage between the two, containing undergrowth and immature trees. Pasture may have been abandoned and allowed to run wild, falling prey to a creeping advance of small trees and shrubs, or woodland has perhaps been hewn down and left for nature to take its course. Without rabbits to keep young saplings nibbled, many areas which were open and fairly stable grassland prior to the myxomatosis epidemics have now reverted to scrub or thicket. Scrub is therefore one of the last rungs in the ladder of plant growth before an area must firmly be classed as woodland.

Hedges

A hedge, in the modern sense, with its accompanying ditch and grassy sward, is nothing more or less than a planted and carefully managed area of scrub, designed largely for the purpose of fencing. It is defined as a row of bushes or low trees, planted closely to form a boundary.

Hedges separating a patchwork quilt of fields are a particularly English phenomenon, begun and slowly

expanded from the Saxon period to restrict the wanderings of livestock, and reaching a zenith with the mainly arable enclosures of the 18th and early 19th centuries. While hedges may be English, lowland field boundaries constructed from living trees and shrubs, with or without a stone wall base, are nonetheless not uncommon features across much of Europe. The word hedge derives from an Anglo-Saxon word *haga* meaning hawthorn, and the traditional hedging species has always been hawthorn (*Crataegus monogyna*), though

Above Privet (*Ligustrum vulgare*) is one of the more recently-favoured hedging plants. A shrub that normally grows in thickets, it is easily managed, providing a dense stock-proof fence.

Left One of the last rungs in the ladder of plant colonization before mature woodland is scrub: land which was once pasture or woodland and now represents an intermediate stage between the two.

in recent times privet (*Ligustrum vulgare*) has become popular. Both species grow casually as scrub and thicket vegetation, but have been used as hedging species because of their robustness, speed of growth, and density when pruned.

Favoured hedging shrubs often bear thorns or spines as an added stockproofing deterrent: the living counterpart to barbed wire! Hedges must be managed constantly to keep them effective, and several techniques are in use. The simplest is to trim the hedging shrubs down to near ground level, which stimulates rich growth from the base. To clip a hedge any higher than a metre is unlikely to be effective. The current labour-effective mechanical trimming is also a poor substitute for hand pruning, and frequently leads to a depleted hedge which has to be complemented with other forms of fencing. The laying of hedges is more time-consuming but highly effective. Traditionally, this method entails cutting partway through the main stems, about 50cm above soil level, and bending them horizontally, each being held in place with binders of willow, ash or hazel. Notice how, in a laid hedge, a rich branching comes from the horizontals, making a much more thorough barrier for stock.

Hedges are often planted at the top of small ridges, created by ditching and banking the earth, and when you survey a typical hedge you need to include the accompanying ditch and sward. In the past, sunken ways were sometimes dug out between fields, and these can still be seen in lowland Britain and parts of Europe as green lanes, providing a trackway with steep sheltered banks on either side.

The hedge is a man-made shelter belt which includes species of open pasture and more delicate woodland plants. It offers shade; it provides ample

Above Hedges should be trimmed in winter months to a height of about a metre in order to keep them stockproof. Formerly, this was done by hand; today, mechanization has taken over, often with poor results as regards the quality of hedge.

Below The most effective method of maintaining a hedge is by laying, but this is a time-consuming and labour-intensive operation. Hedges are laid by cutting partway through the main stems, close to the ground, and bending horizontally.

support for ramblers and climbers; the soil is rich in humus, and the transition from bank to ditch frequently offers a gradation from well-drained to boggy ground. As a botanical study, therefore, a hedge and ditch provides a marvellous habitat. Scrub and thicket offer most of the same benefits, but more haphazardly.

79

DATING HEDGES

Although the more recently-planted hedges are composed uniformly, and perhaps include a single shrub species, early hedges were more rough and ready, put together with whatever material was available close at hand. So how do you tell the approximate age of a hedge? There is a simple and surprisingly effective method of estimating: pace out a 50 metre length of hedge, and then count the number of shrub species growing within the limits. Generally speaking, a recent hedge, planted 100 years ago, will include a single species. A hedge planted 400 years ago will contain four species, and an ancient 1000-year-old hedge will have between nine and twelve. In other words, you can reckon on about one species for every hundred years that the hedge has been in existence.

The main boundary of my garden lies alongside an old coaching road and the hedge includes four species: hawthorn, privet, blackthorn (*Prunus spinosa*) and hazel (*Corylus*). Records confirm that they were probably planted in the late 16th century. Do not be tempted, incidentally, to count occasional bushes and trees that have probably intruded accidently: my hedge also contains an elder tree (*Sambucus nigra*), which I have eliminated from the calculation.

Above Blackthorn (*Prunus spinosa*) is a frequent component of old hedges. The number of species in a length of hedge can be used as a guide to its approximate age.

Right above Occasional trees and bushes, such as elder (*Sambucus nigra*), will invade a hedgerow, but these are not strictly to be included in the calculations of its age.

Left Old hedges will include shrub species in a ratio of approximately one per 100 years. The hedge seen here borders the ancient Fosse Way, an English highway which has been in existence since Roman times. The hedge was probably first planted in the Tudor period.

Older hedges

In older hedges, look out for several typical species which were often planted among hawthorn and privet. Some of these have provided benefits to man other than as fencing material: both the purging buckthorn (*Rhamnus catharticus*) and alder buckthorn (*R. frangula*), for example, possess medicinal properties, and supplied country wives in times gone by with herbal laxatives and purgatives. Other commonly-occurring species are spindle tree (*Euonymus europaeus*), medlar (*Mespilus*), holly (*Ilex aquifolium*) and wayfaring tree (*Viburnum lantana*), and various kinds of *Pyrus*, including pear (*P. communis*), crab apple (*Malus sylvestris*) and rowan (*Sorbus aucuparia*).

Ornamental hedges

Ornamental hedges are often planted with beech (*Fagus*), which tends to retain its leaves throughout the winter, and with evergreens such as yew (*Taxus baccata*), box (*Buxus sempervirens*) and lonicera (*L. xylosteum*), though these are unsuitable for stock control because some of them, yew in particular, produce dangerous poisons in their leaves.

Left Purging buckthorn (*Rhamnus catharticus*) is one of several fencing materials selected because of its thorns, which improve the stock-proofing capability of the hedge. Extracts from the bark were used in times gone by as a herbal laxative.

Right The rowan tree or mountain ash (*Sorbus aucuparia*) is one of the larger of the species that frequent hedgerows. Though its leaves are reminiscent of the ash, it is a member of the rose family, and in autumn it bears clusters of the familiar bright orange-red pomes, mistakenly called 'rowan berries'.

HEDGE ENVIRONMENTS

When considered together, the hedgerows in lowland England constitute the biggest single British nature reserve. In the 1970s there were over half a million miles of hedge still in existence. With an average width of two metres, the area of hedgerow habitat was then about 175,000 hectares, but each year, with the move towards bigger and more efficient fields, thousands of miles are lost forever, grubbed out and replaced by post and pale fences, and by barbed wire. With the modern practice of burning stubble, many hedgerows are also destroyed inadvertently by fire. Where hedges remain, they are often in a dilapidated state, having been left to grow wild. Like all living things hedgerow shrubs come to the end of their natural life and die off, but unless they are replaced by fresh material, the hedge disappears, leaving only the occasional bush and a profusion of brambles and nettles.

Charting a hedge

In effect, a living hedge provides a meeting place of two habitats, woodland and meadow, and contains species from both. If it includes a ditch then there may also be a third, wetland environment. It is important to identify the distinct regions and observe the ways in which they interact with each other. The best way to chart a hedge and ditch is to make a transect through from one side to the other. Before starting, though, you should establish which way the hedge is facing, because the differences in exposure on, let us say, the north and south sides of a hedge will contribute to a noticeable variation in

Below With the advent of barbed wire and large agricultural machinery, the traditional art of maintaining living hedges declined. Small fields are uneconomical, and thousands of miles of hedgerow have been grubbed out or, like this one, left to become dilapidated remnants, no longer serving the purpose for which they were originally intended.

Charting a hedge

Identify the map reference on your proposed chart, date it, and make notes on the orientation, degree of exposure, and factors that might affect the hedge, such as the types of crop being grown on either side, the proximity of a major road, or the existence of industrial pollutants. Select a good representative section of your hedge and make sure that you can gain access to both sides freely. You will need to take more than one – ideally three – transects through the hedge, at approximately 10-metre intervals.

Using a measure to ascertain the details, draw out a ground profile. If there are ditches, indicate the water level in each ditch, whether it is stagnant or flowing, the height and shape of banks, and the relative height of the level ground on either side. If the hedge runs alongside a road, include the verge as far as the hard surface.

Now measure the height of the hedge and draw it in schematically. Note whether it consists of a single or double row of bushes, whether it has been layered, and whether it is trimmed. At the point of your transect, run a piece of string from one margin to the other as a guide (tie a piece of stone or a twig to the end to throw it over or through the hedge).

Carefully identify the plants, progressing from one outer margin through to the other, and draw them in schematically on the transect chart. You may find it easier to list all the plant species and give each a code letter or number. Do not forget to include algae, lichens, mosses, and liverworts in your search. For additional information, try colour coding so that you can distinguish climbers, woodland plants, meadow plants, bog and aquatic species, introductions and hybrids.

Now take a 50-metre stretch of the hedge through which your transects run and list all the species on one side, underlining the dominant types. Repeat the process for the opposite side. Ideally, make separate lists for the hedging species, climbers, other plants in the sub-storeys, ditch plants, and verge plants.

density of the species. Map out the different zones, each providing its own distinct habitat: the sward, constituting a miniature meadow; the ditch, which will be either a damp hollow or filled with water; the well-drained slope, and the protected area immediately beneath the shrubs. For a proper survey you will need to repeat this mapping for both sides of the hedge.

More than with any other habitat, it is valuable to discover the changes that take place in a hedgerow environment through the seasons of a year, because there is always something in a hedge that is coming into leaf or flower. Make a list of the species found in each zone, but then sub-divide them according to seasonal appearance and flowering.

Right Wire fencing and other forms of man-made barrier may require less maintenance in the short term, but they are poor substitutes for a green hedge. They provide no shelter, and generally remain barren and unsightly structures until they rust away.

WALLS

A hedge is not necessarily constructed from shrubs. Since, by definition, it is a fence, it can equally be built from stone. Stone hedges are often constructed where either the degree of exposure or the lack of soil depth make it impractical to plant a living hedge, and these inanimate fences also provide a foundation and framework for a wide variety of plants. Within a year or two, the most inhospitable surface will have provided a base for lichens and mosses. As these die and rot down, they create little pockets of humus in which will appear ferns, grasses, stonecrops and other plants capable of surviving in minimal soil. Dry stone walls are frequently constructed of a double sandwich of rough stones gathered from fields being cleared for cultivation. The sandwich is infilled with soil and small stones from the ditching on either side, and the result is a firm surface with a very well-drained earth core.

Such hedges rapidly become colonized through the germination of seeds, not only from the earth within, but blown into cracks on air currents or deposited by animals. Whether they rest in small pockets of earth, or with their roots buried deep in the wall's core, such plants are inevitably faced with periodical drought, and they show certain common characteristics which help to cope with the problem. Leaves are arranged in flat

rosettes, the under-surfaces lying close to the stone, trapping slightly moister air and so reducing transpiration. Often, the leaves are very small, as is the case with the hair grasses, or modified to store water, as in such species as pennywort (*Cotyledon umbilicus*) and stonecrop (*Sedum*).

One wall colonizer, the ivy-leaved toadflax (*Linaria cymbalaria*), has developed a particularly ingenious device. When the fruits are ripe, their stalks lengthen and develop negative phototropism, bending away

Above Most plants that inhabit walls have to combat physiological drought, because any soil that they find is quickly drained. Stonecrop (*Sedum acre*) is well adapted, having fleshy, water-retaining leaves.

Left Drystone walls are also hedges in the technical sense, constructed where available materials and a high exposure factor make them preferable to living hedgerows. Here Phyllitis grows from between limestone boulders.

Left The wall rue (*Asplenium ruta-muraria*) is one of the hardy ferns that thrive on dry sunny walls. Its leaves are reduced in surface area and tough.

Below Some colonizers of stone walls develop ingenious mechanisms to ensure survival. Ivy-leaved toadflax (*Linaria cymbalaria*) reflexes its ripe fruit stalks back into the wall crevices, where they shed their seeds.

from the light and thus reflexing back into the wall crevices, where the seeds are shed!

The hardy ferns of walls include polypody (*Polypodium*), wall rue (*Asplenium ruta-muraria*) and maidenhair spleenwort (*Asplenium trichomanes*). In places where the walls are more permanently shaded, one of the commonest species is hart's tongue (*Phyllitis scolopendrium*), with its large glossy undivided leaves. With foliage of this kind, the fern would obviously be unable to withstand large amounts of direct sunlight or persistent drying.

Surveying a wall

A wall can be surveyed by making a transect from one side to the other, in precisely the same way as for a living hedge. It is equally necessary to list the plants growing on each side, particularly if the wall faces north and south. Essentially, the species on either side of the wall may be similar, but the dominance and density of occurrence will be different. Shade-loving plants will favour the north face, while the other side will support a predominance of species able to withstand intense light, drought and heat. Often, because of its reflective capacity, a sheltered and south-facing wall in mid-European latitudes will support plants which are more typically seen further south in the sub-tropical, dry, Mediterranean areas.

VERGES

The greensward or verge along the hedge, possibly with an accompanying ditch, supports flora more akin to those of a grassland, but because it lies in the shelter of the hedge's woodland-style habitat and is less likely to be cropped by grazing animals, it is often richer in species than an open meadow. The chief danger to the flowers of a sward, particularly by a roadside, is mowing. At one time, many roadside verges were mown flat with such regularity that wild flowers more or less vanished, but in recent years policies have changed, and now roadside swards offer a riot of blooms through the summer. Those on field boundaries are probably more vulnerable today because of the effects of hedgerow removal, intrusion of cereal grasses, windblown herbicides, and stubble burning.

Verge plants

Verges will support taller species than an open meadow. It is impossible even to begin listing such plants in the space permitted here, but across Europe certain species tend to be particularly prominent. The interest for the botanist is to discover how the different species relate to their environment and to each other, and to note the tendency towards a decline in grassland species and an increase in woodland species as the influence of the hedge becomes stronger. Various common members of the Umbelliferae frequent hedgerows, and these are, by origin, grassland species. All bear flattish showy clusters of small flowers known as *umbels*. Generally, the first to bloom amongst the

Below Among the common umbellifers of roadside verges, cow parsley (*Anthriscus sylvestris*) is the first to bloom, flowering in late spring. Its foliage leaves usually begin to appear in the previous autumn.

Above One of the prettiest of white European hedgerow flowers is the campion species *Lychnis alba*. A coarsely-hairy biennial, it blooms throughout the summer months.

medium-sized white-flower species commonly found along verges is cow parsley (*Anthriscus sylvestris*), followed by rough chervil (*Chaerophyllum temulentum*), with hedge parsley (*Torilis japonica*) flowering last, in high summer. If you find parsley-like leaves carpeting a verge over the winter they will almost certainly be the shoots of cow parsley. The three species often dominate roadside verges and field borders through the late spring and summer.

Other meadow plants, such as thistles and yarrow, may invade the undergrowth of hedges, but you will notice that the stems can become abnormally weak and elongated in an effort to reach up to the sunlight.

In the spring, look out for annual or biennial garlic mustard (*Alliaria officinalis*). It, too, has small white flowers in groups, but it belongs to the Cruciferae family. Its large, heart-shaped and toothed leaves are a give-away feature of a plant which is essentially one from woodland margins, used to growing in fairly shaded conditions. They are quite flimsy, with few defences against intense light and drought. The leaves smell of onion when rubbed between the fingers.

In high summer, other common verge plants are the vetches (*Vicia*), particularly adapted for clambering over other stronger foliage. Red campion (*Lychnis dioica*) and various members of the Labiatae "dead nettle" family, by contrast, develop long tough stalks to compete with high grasses and with each other. The same is true of late summer Compositae species like tansy (*Tanacetum vulgare*), which has button-like composite flowers of a rich yellow, and chicory (*Chichorium intybus*), making a delightful contrast with its brilliant blue blooms. Both are rugged perennials, growing up to a metre tall, with strong resilient rooting systems (chicory has a long tap root) that can withstand any amount of above-ground damage and re-emerge successfully.

Above left Often growing in proximity to its pure white relative, the red campion (*Lychnis dioica*) develops tough erect stems to compete with high hedgerow grasses and other verge plants.

Above right In later summer the brilliant blue flowers of chicory (*Chicorum intybus*) grace European roadsides. A rugged perennial with tough resilient roots, it can withstand regular mowing.

If the verge area has been disturbed, as often happens during road widening, red poppies and ragworts will make a rapid appearance, but within one or two seasons they will be ousted by the more permanent perennials, with their stronger rooting systems.

Scrubland

Scrubland is, in effect, a less ordered combination of hedge and verge. Like so many habitats, it is not a permanent state, and just as there is an ordered succession of plants that will gradually colonize bare ground, so there will be a succession as the habitat approaches its permanent state of woodland.

This means that if you are able to survey an area of this type over a 10-year period, starting with bare soil, you will see it evolve into grassland, then scrub, and finally thicket. Where, for example, an area of ground has been burnt, fire moss (*Funaria*) will survive for two or three seasons at most before it is ousted by grasses. Similarly, low-growing and rosette plants will eventually be replaced by taller species, as plants reach higher and higher in competition for the light.

Above In more shaded hedgerow locations, the hedge garlic or garlic mustard (*Alliaria officinalis*) bears clusters of small white flowers in late spring. The delicate heart-shaped leaves smell of garlic when crushed.

CLIMBERS

Amongst the most notable colonizers of hedges are *climbers*. Any plant that takes root in the shelter of a hedge either tolerates shady conditions, or it needs to manoeuvre its foliage leaves into a position where they can compete with those of the more dominant plants to receive proper illumination. In the latter situation, many plants use the framework of the hedge to climb, often considerable distances, on weak straggly stems. With such plants, the leaves are not necessarily smaller, but they are more widely separated because the stems elongate by extension of the internodes. Without a supporting ladder, the plants would adopt a prostrate lifestyle, spreading along the ground. For the botanist, the interest is not merely one of identifying such plants, but of discovering the different techniques they develop for climbing.

There is a distinction between plants which *climb*, and those which *twine*. Climbers use special organs such as hooks and tendrils on stems and leaves. Twiners rely solely on the twisting of their stems to loop round a supporting framework. One of the commonest of the woody climbing plants is honeysuckle (*Lonicera periclymenum*). Related to the free-standing shrub *L. xylosteum* , honeysuckle, with its weak stems, has

Above Among the hedgerow climbers, black bryony (*Tamus cammunis*) negotiates its way upwards to the light, using stems that twine clockwise around stronger supports. Its bright red berries provide a distinctive autumn feature.

Left Honeysuckle (*Lonicera periclymenum*) twines tightly around stronger stems and can use them to attain considerable height in a hedgerow or tree.

Left One of the commonest of hedgerow climbers is wild clematis or old man's beard (*Clematis vitalba*). Its showy flowers are borne on stems that are sometimes massive, and are supported initially by twining leaf petioles that grasp more rigid frameworks.

sacrificed strength for length. Look closely at the tip of a honeysuckle shoot which is standing free – it is not straight, but follows a loose clockwise spiral (when viewed from above). When the tip makes contact with a support of suitable diameter it begins to twine around it and as it does so, the spiral becomes constricted, clasping the support tightly and becoming thicker and stronger so that it cannot unwind.

Several twining members of the *Polygonum* family, including black bindweed (*P. convolvulus*) and the Russian vine (*P. baldschuanicum*), are frequent residents in a hedge. These are herbaceous annuals which, like the honeysuckle, possess clockwise twisting stems. Other clockwise twiners often to be seen in hedges include black bryony (*Tamus communis*) and hop (*Humulus lupulus*). Other twiners, including the bindweeds of the family *Convolvulus* and the parasitic climber, dodder (*Cuscuta*), develop an anti-clockwise movement.

Petioles and tendrils

One of the more massive European climbing plants is the wild clematis or old man's beard (*C. vitalba*). This plant does not climb by means of its stems, which can grow to several metres in length and up to 8cm thick, scrambling over large shrubs and small trees, but with the stalks of its large pinnate leaves, which can grasp on to suitable supports. These leaf *petioles* twist around shoots and branches of suitable size.

Sometimes, as in the case of the vetches (*Vicia*), it is not the petiole but part of the leaf itself which does the twining, by changing into a tendril. The bush vetch (*V. sepium*) is frequent in hedgerows across Europe. Each common leaf stalk, from which the leaflets arise, has its terminal leaflet replaced by a twining tendril. Around the Mediterranean regions, climbing fumitory (*Fumaria capreolata*) with its white or rose-red flowers climbs by similar means. More severe reduction occurs in the pea family (*Lathyrus*) – the everlasting pea (*L. sylvestris*) has only a single pair of leaflets and long branching tendrils. If you look at the stems, you will see that because the leaf surface has been so much reduced, some of the responsibility for photosynthesis has been taken over by the stems and petioles. Normally more or less rounded in cross-section, the tissues have grown unevenly into extended ridges running lengthwise and generally referred to as "wings". The ridges offer a greatly enlarged surface area to receive sunlight and are packed with cells that operate as a major food synthesizing area of the plant.

Other climbers, including white bryony (*Bryonia dioica*), develop tendrils in the leaf axils. These are technically modified stems rather than leaves. Vines (*Vitis*) attach themselves by similar means, the tendrils sometimes bearing small scaly leaves which give away their true identity as stems. Stem tendrils work in much the same way as those of leafy origin, twisting around a support when their tips make contact.

Above White bryony (*Bryonia dioica*) is unrelated, other than in name, to black bryony. A member of the cucumber family, it climbs by means of tendrils that develop in the axils of its large distinctive leaves.

Below Hooks are valuable climbing aids. Small enough to be felt rather than seen, those of goosegrass (*Galium aparine*) enable weak straggling stems to reach a height of a metre or more.

Roots and hooks

Ivy (*Hedera helix*) develops a massive structure and often climbs great distances, clinging by special root-like structures on the stems. These *adventitious roots*, which embed themselves in the surface of the support and act as grips, are not parasitic structures; they draw no nourishment from the host, though they can cause structural damage by forcing their way into cracks in masonry.

Plants of a climbing habit may also be reliant on various types of *hook* to achieve their ends. All the climbing and rambling members of the rose family, including the wild roses (*Rosa*) and brambles (*Rubus*), develop sharp prickles on their stems. Goosegrass (*Galium aparine*) is a weak climbing annual which can, nonetheless, clamber to a metre or more in a hedgerow, using small versions of hook which develop not only on the angles of the stems but also on the midribs and the edges of leaves.

Below The hooks on the dogrose (*Rosa canina*) are sharp, stout, reddish-coloured prickles, and enable the plant to ascend to the top of a hedgerow.

Parthenocissus tricuspidata (Virginia creeper) utilizes sticky discs at the end of leaf tendrils.

Lonicera periclymenum (honeysuckle) climbs by clockwise stem twisting.

Hedera helix (ivy) climbs by means of adventitious roots along its stems.

Lathyrus spp (pea) climb by means of twining leaf tendrils.

Right Climbers resort to a variety of mechanical means to carry their typically weak stems up to the light. Some twine their stems, or highly modified stems and leaves while others rely on special roots or suckers.

PLANT MOVEMENTS

It may be difficult to think of plants moving actively, yet many do so. Among the more obvious examples are the delightful little spring woodland sorrel (*Oxalis acetosella*), which closes its trefoil leaves at night in a sleep position, and the Mediterranean mimosa (*Mimosa pudica*), which shows the same darkness reaction but also closes its leaves rapidly in a defence response when shocked.

Many flowers open and close in response to temperature change, including members of the crocus family and such spring flowers as lesser celandine (*Ranunculus ficaria*). The common sundew (*Drosera rotundifolia*), in common with most other insectivorous plants, responds to touch and to chemical stimulus. When a fly is caught in the sticky secretions of the hairs which fringe the leaves, the hairs bend inwards.

Climbing plants show a range of movements. Because of the difficulties in obtaining maximum benefit from light that reaches them from one side only,

Left Like many climbing plants, the white bryony (*Bryonia dioica*) develops weak stems which are unable to support their own weight. Here, the tendrils can be seen clearly.

Right The delicate little wood sorrel (*Oxalis acetosella*) responds to the onset of darkness by closing its leaves into a "sleep" position. At daybreak they start to open again.

Above Many flowers, including the lesser celandine (*Ranunculus ficaria*), protect their flowers by responding to changes in temperature: the petals close if the temperature drops too low.

Below Until they break through the surface, young shoots rely on negative geotropism to guide them upwards, whilst roots rely on positive geotropism.

species inhabiting hedgerows and walls are often particularly sophisticated in such abilities. As with many other plants, they exhibit subtle movements, including the gradual turning of flowers and leaves with the sun, to obtain the best illumination at different times of the day. The best way to observe this effect is to look at the leaves of a climber in a hedge – black bryony, with its large glossy heart-shaped leaves, would be a good example. The upper surfaces, their thick cuticles well proofed against excessive transpiration, are all turned towards the light. If you re-arrange a piece of leafy stem so that the upper leaf surfaces are turned inwards and then leave it for several days, you will discover that the leaves have twisted round again. This movement is called *positive phototropism*. The same phenomenon takes place if a young plant, such as a broad bean, is positioned in a sunny window, in which case you will see that the stem will bend towards the light. In this example, the movement results from unequal growth, the side of the stem away from the light growing faster than that on the window side. If it is the leaves that move, this is because the sides of the petioles are growing at uneven rates. *Contact stimulus*, similar to that used by insectivorous plants, is largely responsible for the coiling movement of tendrils. As the tendril comes into contact with a solid body, the side away from contact is encouraged to grow faster.

Gravity responses

A more dramatic movement in twining stems is attributable to gravity response. The circular motion of the stem is probably a spontaneous occurrence in all plants, but it happens to be more pronounced in twiners. If you find a section of *Convolvulus* twining round a support which can be conveniently turned

upside down, you will discover that after a day or so the tip of the shoot will uncoil from its inverted support, straighten out, take a U-turn, and begin to coil around the support in an upward direction again!

This is called *negative geotropism* – an urge to grow in a direction opposite to the force of gravity. It is the stimulus that keeps most plants pointing upwards as their shoots develop under the soil, and which will cause the sprouting plumule of a seed, planted upside down, to turn around and face the correct way in its search for the surface.

Positive geotropism, a stimulus that encourages movement in the direction of gravity, is responsible, by contrast, for roots growing predominantly downwards.

FRUITS AND SEEDS

Hedgerow and scrub are ideal places to investigate fruits and seeds and their methods of spreading. Because of the shelter provided by the hedge, and the great variety of animal life which takes refuge there, there is a marked tendency for the permanent plants of the hedge to develop fleshy fruits with bright colours that are attractive and palatable to birds and mammals. Both white and black bryony (unrelated) bear bright red berries, as do honeysuckle, rose, spindle tree, hawthorn, and many more. Other fruits may be black or dark blue, but they are often invitingly fleshy and shiny, like those of blackberry, privet and the buckthorns.

A *fruit* is the result of fertilization of the flower, a combination of ovary and fertilized seeds, sometimes with the inclusion of other parts of the flower, most commonly the receptacle. The way fruits are constructed varies, but all fruits can be conveniently separated according to whether they are fleshy or dry.

The amateur may instinctively label all small fleshy fruits as berries, but for a botanist many of these will be drupes or pomes! In addition, one must distinguish simple fruits from compound fruits. The only sure way to discover the essential differences between them is to draw the fruits, both whole and cut open, to reveal the internal structure.

Drupes and pomes

A *drupe* is a juicy fruit consisting of a hard stone surrounded by the outer layers of the ovary wall, which have become swollen and fleshy. The commonest examples in the hedgerow are the plums and cherries, including the sloe (*Prunus spinosa*) and the wild cherry (*P. cerasus*). Amongst the larger juicy drupes are apricots (*P. armeniaca*) and peaches (*Amygdalus*). Almonds, walnuts and coconuts are also drupes, though in this case the juicy flesh has been reduced to a tough or fibrous skin.

Above The familiar fruits of the wild plum or sloe (*Prunus spinosa*) are drupes, in which the innermost part of the ovary wall becomes hard and stony and the outparts are swollen and juicy.

Left The spindle tree (*Euonymus europaeus*) develops distinctive pink fruits in the form of fleshy capsular pods, typically with four lobes. These open when ripe by means of valves, liberating the seeds.

Pomes include an assortment of fruits which may, at first glance, seem to possess little in common, but which are all linked by similar construction. Hawthorn berries, rose hips, and the apple and pear fruits, such as quince, medlar, and rowan, are all pomes. No part of the ovary containing the seeds becomes fleshy, but it remains as the tough core, around which the receptacle of the flower expands to form the edible part of the fruit. Sometimes, as in the hawthorn pome, the inner part becomes stony, but although it might be confused with a drupe, it has a quite different construction.

Berries

Most of the rest of the fleshy fruits in the hedgerow are *berries*, similar in construction to the drupe but without a stony inner lining, the seeds being embedded directly in the pulp. One of the oddest, if not the most striking of the berry-producing plants, lurks in the shady undergrowth at the base of the hedge. The arum lily (*Arum maculatum*) fruits develop as a spike of green berries which ripen to a bright orange red. Many of the small berries growing wild in a hedge have relatives that are

Below A humble and mildly poisonous relative of the tomato, bittersweet (*Solanum dulcamara*) produces clusters of berries – similar to drupes but without a stony inner part – which ripen to a bright red.

Right The gladdon or roastbeef plant (*Iris foetidissima*) occurs in shady places throughout western Europe. Its fruit is a capsule that splits open to reveal rows of bright orange or scarlet fleshy seeds.

familiar in the garden or the greengrocers. The white bryony (*Bryonia dioica*) is a member of the cucumber family, and woody nightshade (*Solanum dulcamara*), which often scrambles about in the lower part of a hedge, is a humble and inedible cousin of the tomato. Grapes and oranges are also cultivated forms of berry.

Blackberry (*Rubus*) and wild strawberry (*Fragaria*) are examples of compound fruits. A blackberry is a collection of small drupes or drupelets, all fused together on the receptacle, while a strawberry is a collection of non-fleshy single seeds, or *achenes*, embedded in the surface of a massive juicy receptacle which has swelled up in the middle. An achene is a fruit in its simplest form. It is dry (i.e. no part becomes fleshy or juicy) and consists of a single seed surrounded by the ovary wall – the simplest examples are to be found in the buttercups (*Ranunculus*).

Juicy fruits are designed for one purpose – to appeal to the tastes of hedgerow gourmets! Birds and mammals are lured by colour, texture and flavour to eat the fleshy pulp and, in doing so, to ingest the seeds, to deposit them elsewhere, or discard them.

95

SEED DISPERSAL

The seeds of juicy fruits are thus equipped for *animal dispersal*. In most types of fruit the means is immaterial biologically, but in the compound fruits it is essential that the seeds are liberated one from another, and the best means of achieving this objective is through animal ingestion.

Non-juicy fruits are generally dispersed by wind action, or by becoming attached to the coats of passing animals. Wind-spread fruits are dry as distinct from fleshy, and they often possess extensions which enable them to float on air currents. Some wind-spread seeds, for example those of the orchids, are so tiny that they blow about freely in the breeze without requiring further modification.

Dry fruits

The most obvious illustration of a hedgerow fruit equipped with special apparatus for wind dispersal is clematis (*C. vitalba*). The single-seeded fruits or *achenes* are carried by means of long feathery extensions which derive from the style above the ovary.

Members of the Compositae, including dandelions and thistles, disperse their fruits typically on a fan of hairs, the *pappus*, which in origin is a modified calyx.

Many trees develop a fruit known as *samara*. This is a simple one-seeded arrangement, in which the wall of the fruit extends as a wing which helps the seed to move with the wind. Relying on its wing, it can flutter some distance before it lands. In the *Acer* species there is a *double samara*, which separates after dispersal.

Flowers which have many-seeded fruits often develop *capsules* from which the seeds escape. Poppy seeds are shaken out through little pores. Other capsules, like those produced by the balsams (*Impatiens*), liberate seeds in a more violent manner – the capsules burst into valves which roll inwards, scattering the seeds.

Below Dry fruits of thistles such as *Carduus lanceolatus*, which are members of the Compositae family, are spread on fans of hairs – the pappi – which are caught up by the air currents.

Right The seeds of willowherbs, including rosebay (*Epilobium angustifolium*), are shed from pods which unpeel like a banana when ripe. Plumes of long silky hairs ensure efficient wind-dispersal.

Above Burdock (*Arctium lappa*) produces composite flowers with hooked bracts; these can catch on to the fur of a passing animal and carry the ripe fruit away.

Below The hooks on the fruits of teasel (*Dipsascus fullonium*) act only as a trigger, catching on animal fur, pulling the seed head over, and then, when released, catapulting the seeds free.

The Cruciferae rely on fruits known as the *silicula* and the *siliqua*. Shepherd's purse (*Capsella bursa-pastoris*) bears typical siliculas. The seeds are attached to a membrane running down the middle of a flattened and rather squat fruit, and on either side are flaps of ovary wall which, when the seeds are ripe, break away, starting at the base. Siliquas are more elongated but operate on the same mechanical principle and are most commonly seen in the wallflower (*Cheiranthus*) and in cabbage-type plants (*Brassica*).

Nuts are dry one-seeded fruits, in which the ovary wall has become tough or woody, and they are also reliant largely on animals for dispersal. In the hazel (*Corylus*), the nut is enclosed in a membranous sheath of special protective bracts called the *cupule*. The same structure occurs in oak (*Quercus*) and beech (*Fagus*), but in these species the cupule is woody.

There are, incidentally, some confusing peculiarities to watch out for. Sweet chestnut (*Castanea*) fruits are nuts contained in leathery *cupules*. Horse chestnut (*Aesculus*) fruits are *capsules* in which all but one seed has aborted!

Finally, look out for fruits designed to be carried on the backs of animals. The burdock (*Arctium*) bears a composite flower made up of florets and bracts. The bracts become hooked, and after the flower withers the whole apparatus can catch on animal fur and be carried away. Goosegrass (*Galium*) fruit bears small hooks, as does that of enchanter's nightshade (*Circaea*). Teasel (*Dipsascus*) offers a variation on the theme in that the hooks on the seed head are designed to catch on animals and be dragged over, so that when the head recoils the seeds are catapulted out.

WETLANDS, SEASHORES AND DUNES
INTRODUCTION

The three habitats in this section are linked only because of their association with water, but as physiological environments for plants, each is distinct. In a freshwater habitat, the water acts as a solvent for inorganic salts drawn from the soil or rocks on which it is based. These chemical compounds include sulphates and carbonates of calcium, sodium, potassium, magnesium and iron, plus traces of many other elements. The essential distinction between sea and freshwater lies in the fact that freshwater contains a much lower concentration of dissolved elements than that found in the sea. Consequently, the osmotic pressures exerted on living organisms in fresh and salt waters are quite different. Some plants can cope with marked fluctuations in the salinity of their water. These include species living in brackish waters and salt-marshes. In most cases, however, the plants of one habitat will not survive the conditions of another.

A wetland, in the accepted sense, is an area governed by freshwater. It can be a spring emerging from under a rock, a mountain torrent, a lowland river gliding along sedately, a vast inland lake, a small stagnant ditch or a bog. Temperate Europe, like other

Left It is important to evaluate an aquatic habitat: is it the source of a stream or river, the bedrock, or the bottom; what is the degree of flow; is there vegetation on the banks; is the water saline and does it contain effluents?

Above Waterfalls offer a habitat with very peculiar characteristics, and plants that survive must be well adapted to cope with the rigorous nature of their surroundings.

comparable climatic regions of the globe, enjoys a profusion of fresh inland water, and the habitat encourages plant colonization in a variety and density offered by few other natural situations. Some of the very earliest forms of life arose in fresh water and many of them, including the algae, still persist, but the aquatic habit also supports some of the most sophisticated plants, among which a number have returned to water to escape competition on land.

The type and modification of aquatic plants varies according to the nature of the water they inhabit. Thus, the plants clinging to a waterfall will not, as a rule,

Right Estuaries – the regions where sea and freshwater habitats find an interface – will only support plants that are capable of withstanding alternating saline and brackish water. These are also the stretches of any river system that are most prone to pollution.

Below The depth of water in a lake and the degree of surface wind action both contribute to the type of habitat that results. Depth, in particular, is significant because it affects both the degree of light reaching the bottom and the water temperature.

be found on a slower-flowing river bed, and will be different again from those floating freely in a pond. Each habitat is colonized by species that are adapted to benefit from its particular conditions.

Assessing the conditions

A waterfall, a river, or a lake may seem like a fairly predictable environment, but with any freshwater it is important for the botanist to examine it first for its overall conditions. Taking a river as an example, is it fast or slow moving? What is the nature of the bottom – rocky, gravelly, or muddy? Is it a chalk stream with alkaline content, or an acid peat water flowing over granite? Is the flow tidal, in which case where is the upper limit of saltwater incursion? Is the river subject to effluent pollution? If so, in what respects does its character alter above and below the point of discharge?

The same kind of evaluation is needed for other aquatic habitats in order to establish basic facts: the chemical nature of the water; whether it benefits from a flow or is totally stagnant; the kind of overhanging vegetation which may influence the amount of light; the wind action, and the build-up of organic rubbish. It is also necessary to look at seasonal changes. Does the habitat dry up in long hot spells, or if near a tidal river, does the flow reverse? The depth of the water is also significant, because it affects variables such as light intensity and temperature.

LAKES

The physical nature of a lake needs to be established. The approximate pH can be gauged by purchasing a simple and inexpensive soil-testing kit from any large garden centre. In a shallow lake, wind action mixes the water fairly evenly, thus stirring up the salts, which are concentrated most heavily at the bottom, and providing an even temperature from surface to bed. Such lakes are *eutrophic* – often with a broad shore region, neutral or slightly alkaline pH, rich in mineral salts and nutrients, and therefore enjoying luxuriant plant growth.

Dystrophic lakes, typical of boggy moorland regions, may be equally shallow and experience thorough water mixing. However, they are very acid, with little plant growth, but large amounts of humus.

Oligotrophic lakes are deep with very narrow shores. This produces an effect called a thermocline. Anyone who has swum in summer in a deep lake may have experienced this at first hand when their legs suddenly penetrate from a pleasant temperature to what feels like freezing cold water! A warm but nutrient-deficient layer stays at the surface, separated from the mass of very cold water below. This deeper body is rich in dissolved minerals but because it is only partially stirred up by wind action (and then only in winter), and is too dark and cold for plant growth, oligotrophic lakes support little plant growth.

Above Water that is dystrophic, a condition which is typical of expanses of standing water in boggy moorland regions, may be shallow, with a good mixing of layers, but the pH tends to be acidic, and large amounts of humus collect. Typically the water is discoloured to a peaty brown, and plant life is minimal. Great care should be taken when wading into dystrophic lakes, since the bottom may be extremely unstable.

Surveying lakes

Lakes are difficult and dangerous areas to survey without specialized equipment. A boat is necessary, and this must be properly equipped with life-saving apparatus. Unless the water is very clear, you may also require qualified sub-aqua assistance. Working from a boat, providing that the bottom of the lake is visible, you should make a chart that relates species with the depth of water at which they are growing. The surface-to-bottom depth must first be measured at regular distances from the water margin, until the point at which plant life ceases. This enables you to draw a transect.

The aquatic and marginal plant species can now be added to the chart, either by identifying them from the surface of the water, or by raking up samples. It is important to note such factors as the maximum depth at which bottom-rooted species possess floating leaves. Results will show that species occur in zones relating to depth.

Right Eutrophic lakes are typical of lowlands, and are the richest in plant life out of three physiological types of lake. Their pH is generally near to neutral and the shore regions are shallow, ensuring good mixing.

Below Oligotrophic lakes, such as those in the English Lake District, are characterized by considerable depth and narrow shore lines. This can produce marked temperature variations between surface and deeper layers known as the thermocline.

AQUATIC ADAPTATIONS

Aquatic plants can be distinguished according to whether they are free-floating, submerged, but with their reproductive organs emerging into the air, or totally immersed. There are also amphibious species that inhabit the water's edge and are essentially land plants, used to life in the air, and with little more than their roots in water. True aquatic plants are known as *hydrophytes*. Those of the water margins are technically described as *amphibians*.

Flotation apparatus

One of the vital necessities for an aquatic plant is that its shoots must be able to float efficiently. Water is much more buoyant than air, but the plant still needs its own flotation apparatus or it would lie on the bottom, become damaged by currents and possibly covered with mud, and it would also tend to suffer from less light. To avoid these problems, aquatic plants develop buoyancy chambers, the tissues being arranged in a honeycomb structure called *aerenchyma* – groups of cells between which large air spaces form.

The construction is important for other reasons, too. If the plant is totally submerged, it cannot transpire efficiently. Its roots are particularly vulnerable to oxygen starvation because they penetrate mud that is generally depleted of air. The continuous spaces in the tissues allow gases to circulate freely within the plant organs.

Some bottom-rooted plants, such as the water lilies (*Nuphar lutea* and *Nymphaea alba*) and the free-floating frogbit (*Hydrocharis morsus-ranae*), develop raft-like leaves that rest on the water surface and allow for effective transpiration. Lilies have highly elastic leaf petioles so that even though a plant is firmly anchored the pads can stay afloat when the water level rises.

Many aquatics, such as the water crowfoot (*Ranunculus aquatilis*), possess more than one type of leaf. The plant develops flat, regular, flotation leaves at the surface, and deeply-cut submerged fronds, which are more able to withstand the rigours of living in water currents. This condition is known as *heterophylly*.

Because of the buoyancy of water, a submerged plant needs very little by way of support, so hydrophytes develop almost none of the strengthening tissues found in a land plant and rely almost entirely on their aerenchyma tissues to maintain shape. In a

Left *Nymphaea alba*, the white water lily, can adjust to variations in depth of water. It is rooted in the bottom, but the leaf stalks are elasticated so that the plate-like leaves can float on the surface at all times.

Right Shallow lowland streams typically become choked with vegetation in high summer and can stagnate as a result. A constant supply of nutrients, combined with the shallow depth, provide ideal conditions for a wide range of aquatic and marginal plants.

Below Aquatic plants are designed so that their green shoots will float. The internal anatomy includes honeycomb structures known as aerenchyma tissue, in which the living cells are arranged in chains and are separated by large spaces.

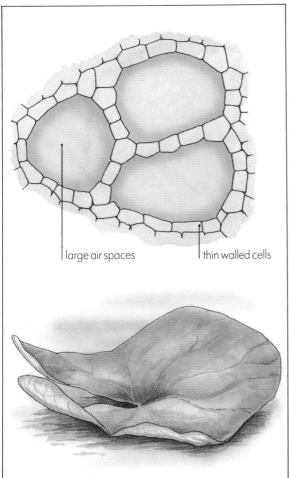

large air spaces   thin walled cells

watery environment, mineral salts and carbon dioxide for photosynthesis can be freely absorbed in solution over all the surfaces, as a result of which transportation systems – xylem and phloem – are also reduced to a minimum. Mineral salts, though, are often present in very fine dilutions, and an aquatic plant must therefore present the largest possible leaf surfaces in order to absorb nutrients, which is another reason why submerged leaves tend to be divided into fine segments. Unlike a land plant, which uses its roots to draw in soluble mineral nutrients, roots are of value to a hydrophyte only as anchors, and in the case of free-floating plants even this function has become completely redundant.

The limited supply of important minerals in some waters has encouraged a very small number of aquatic plants to supplement their diet by developing an insectivorous habit. The free-floating bladderwort (*Utricularia*) which can survive in deep oligotrophic lakes, traps small insects in the many bladders which appear on its finely divided leaves.

Propagation methods

A peculiar problem faced by all aquatic plants is seed production, because pollination is only rarely effective underwater. Some hydrophytes develop special flowering stems designed to operate in air, but almost all back up this option with efficient means of vegetative propagation. Many aquatics develop extensive systems of rhizomes, which penetrate rapidly through the

mud and generate a profusion of aerial shoots. In this way a whole lake bed can become carpeted with Canadian pondweed (*Elodea canadensis*) without the plant producing a single flower.

Even when aquatic plants form flowers, their maturation is much more hazardous than in land plants, and annual hydrophytes cannot rely on dormant seeds to see them through the winter. Instead, in autumn, many develop special overwintering buds called *turions*. These are, in effect, survival capsules: axial buds, protected and nourished by fleshy scale leaves, which sink into the mud and lie dormant ready to germinate in the spring. Turions arise in a range of aquatics extending from the pondweeds (*Potamogeton*), which

Above Reed beds are typical of shallow swampy areas of water. Thanks to their invasive rhizome systems, reed species can rapidly colonize large areas to the exclusion of other marginal and marsh plants.

live entirely submerged, to such free-floating species as frogbit (*Hydrocharis*).

Both turions and seeds are designed to float; they may have protective slimy coverings, and seeds often possess air bags in their coats. Each can secrete sticky substances over their surfaces and this enables them to adhere to the feathers of water birds, assisting dispersal, which often takes place over long distances.

TYPES OF AQUATIC PLANT

If your botanical researches are going to take you to watery habitats, it is important to be able to distinguish the different categories of aquatics. Totally submerged forms include the *Elodea* species and hornwort (*Ceratophyllum*); these forms occasionally produce flowers designed to be self-pollinated under water, but the flowers are difficult to find and are rarely developed.

They are small, sessile, and form in the leaf axils. Among the common examples of true water plants (as distinct from marginals), which root in the bottom but develop leaves and flowering shoots that break through the surface into air are the lilies (*Nuphar* and *Nymphaea*) and water crowfoot (*Ranunculus aquatilis*).

Plants that live in deeper water and produce only flowers that surface are pondweeds (*Potamogeton*) and millfoils (*Myriophyllum*). Among the free-floating plants, frogbit (*Hydrocharis*) uses its leaves as supporting rafts for its flowering shoots. Even duckweed (*Lemna*), which spreads almost wholly by vegetative budding, will very occasionally produce minute colourless flowers at the surface.

Shallow streams, particularly those running over chalk, are often almost blocked by such species as watercress (*Nasturtium officinale*), with its tiny white flowers, and brooklime (*Veronica beccabunga*), which produces a profusion of small blue flowers on thick erect branches.

It is outside the scope of this book to look closely at algae that inhabit freshwater, apart from distinguishing the unicellular forms, such as *Chlamydamonas* and *Euglena*, and filamentous strands, such as *Spirogyra* and *Oedogonium*. Look out also for the fat crinkly strings of *Enteromorpha* found in brackish water and tidal stretches.

At least one moss, *Fontinalis*, is specially adapted to live in fast currents and is often found on waterfalls, mixed with the alga *Vaucheria*. There is also a small species of fern, *Azolla*, which is wholly aquatic and floats on the surface of still waters, forming enormous mats that can sometimes cover a whole pond.

Above The watercress (*Nasturtium officinale*) frequents shallow, slow-flowing streams. It produces small white airborne flowers. A member of the Cruciferae family, it has sometimes been mistaken for the umbellifer, fool's watercress, which has leaves of a similar shape.

Left Often growing in the same habitat as watercress is brooklime (*Veronica beccabunga*). Its blue flowers are borne on fleshy sprawling stems.

AMPHIBIOUS PLANTS

The water margins are colonized by different species of plants from those that live in the body of the water. The range of amphibious species is also determined by the pH of the soil. Hence, the edges of dystrophic lakes, with their high acidity, often support extensive areas of the bog moss *Sphagnum*, while eutrophic waters are fringed by an assortment of marginals, including amphibious bistort (*Polygonum amphibium*), yellow flag (*Iris pseudacorus*), arrowhead (*Sagittaria*), water plantain (*Alisma*) and the flowering rush (*Butomus*). Where the margin extends into a wet meadow, the beautiful golden-flowered marsh marigold (*Caltha palustris*) may spread in extensive clumps.

Marginal and marsh plants

Marginal and marsh plants are equipped to thrive in the halfway house between land and water. Their upper parts have to cope with the same conditions as a true land plant, while their roots and lower stems are frequently standing in water or in poorly-aerated mud. As a result of this, many retain aerenchyma tissue. If you examine the leaves of marsh plants, you will find evidence of this dual nature. Meadowsweet (*Spiraea ulmaria*), for example, which bears beautiful creamy flowers with an unmistakable fragrance, shows an interesting gradation: the lower leaves possess few

hairs, since they are surrounded by moist air, but the upper leaves are hairy, reducing transpiration loss.

Apart from rivers, aquatic habitats are rarely permanent features of the landscape. Eventually, if left unmanaged, most lakes fill up with sediment and organic debris, becoming ever more shallow and turning into swamps, then into bogs or marshes. When this happens, the vegetation that takes over includes many of the marginals, but is successively dominated by swamp plants and then by marshland species. An acid pond, at the end of its life, will thus become a sphagnum bog, often forming vast peat deposits, built up as the moss dies off each season. Eutrophic lakes destined to become swamps develop reed beds, which

Above Many plants fall into a category that is neither truly land-living nor aquatic. These are classed as amphibians and include the marsh marigold (*Caltha palustris*). One of the most beautiful of early summer blooms in wetlands, its fine golden flowers give it the common name of "king cups".

Left The predominant trees of marsh are alders (*Alnus*), though birch (*Betula*) will also tolerate waterlogged ground. The appearance of trees marks the final stage in the evolution from open water to dry land.

encroach progressively as the water becomes shallower. Reed species tend to occur in zones, however. Adjacent to the open water, *Scirpus lacustris* may be present, but it is generally thinly dispersed. Moving towards the shore, the bulk of the reed bed in clear water is commonly made up from *Phragmites communis*. If the water is polluted, though, the dominant species are often reed maces, *Typha latifolia* or *T. angustifolia*.

Reeds

All the reed-type swamp plants grow with long unbranched upright stems, which are held in place by a massive system of creeping rhizomes that invade virtually the whole area of mud, to the exclusion of other vegetation. For this reason, most reed beds are more or less single-species communities. They also play a significant part in the progress towards the formation of dry land, particularly at river and stream inlets, because the reed beds form effective filters, stemming the flow of silt and mud, and their rotting remains each year allow the banks to push further and further into what was originally open water. Some are capable of pumping oxygen into their roots and thus provide a degree of pollution control.

To the landward side of the reeds, conditions merge progressively towards those on normal dry land, and in the marshy zone between, one finds yellow flags (*Iris pseudacorus*), sedges (*Carex*) and rushes (*Juncus*). Certain trees are particularly suited to growing with their roots in wet ground: the various willow species (*Salix*), for example, are common along water margins, and in marshy ground the first trees to become established are usually alder (*Alnus*) and alder buckthorn (*Rhamnus*).

Above *Juncus effusus* is one of the commonest rushes. Its tapered cylindrical stems bear no proper leaves and the regularly formed flowers (unlike grasses and sedges) are in small tufted clusters.

Below Among the prettiest of flowers to grace the water margins, the yellow flag (*Iris pseudoacorus*) is a typical colonizer of the marshy ground surrounding eutrophic lakes.

Above Among the most common mosses of acidic marshland is bog feather. This can clothe the edges of shallow lakes, often in the company of sphagnum.

TRANSECTING A DITCH

One of the most accessible habitats on which to make a transect survey is a ditch. You will probably need a pair of waist-high wading boots if you are to make a thorough investigation, and take care to test out the firmness of the bottom before putting your weight on it – soft mud can be a metre deep and it may be extremely difficult to extricate yourself.

In a typical lowland ditch with a minimal water flow, the deepest part, which lies in the centre, is often colonized by Canadian pond weed (*Elodea*), millfoils (*Myriophyllum*) and hornwort (*Ceratophyllum*). To either side will be the pondweeds (*Potamogeton*) and starwort (*Callitriche*), interspersed with lilies. Standing in the shallows may be water soldier (*Stratioides*), arrowhead (*Sagittaria*), water plantain (*Alisma*) and water dropwort (*Oenanthe*). Floating freely, you may discover an assortment of algae, duckweed (*Lemna*), frogbit (*Hydrocharis*) and perhaps the fern *Azolla*.

Notice how water plants with large, shading, umbrella-like leaves, or those which form a dense mat on the surface, obscure light to the detriment of anything living below.

Frequently, if you peel back a surface coating of duckweed, the water beneath will be barren. The density with which some plant communities develop on the mud floor encourages intensely stagnant zones.

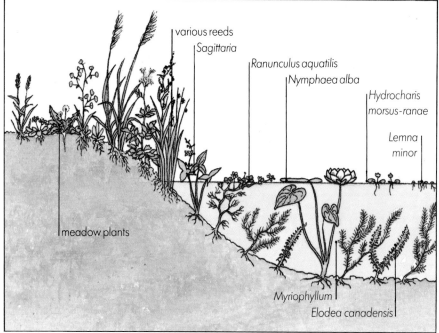

Above Water dropwort (*Oenanthe*) often stands in dense clumps in shallow lowland ditches. An umbellifer with large white flower heads, it should be handled with care as it is poisonous.

Left Transecting a ditch is one of the simplest ways of approaching freshwater surveys. The water is generally fairly shallow and accessible and can offer a range from marginals to free-floating forms within a confined area.

various reeds
Sagittaria
Ranunculus aquatilis
Nymphaea alba
Hydrocharis morsus-ranae
Lemna minor
meadow plants
Myriophyllum
Elodea canadensis

Above Not to be confused with rosebay willowherb, the purple loosestrife (*Lythrum salicaria*) bears fine purple flowers in long spikes and is widespread on the margins of fresh waters.

Left You can generally smell meadowsweet (*Spiraea ulmaria*) before you see it! Its distinctive fragrance (reminiscent of vanilla) complements the beautiful creamy clusters of tiny flowers.

Left Slow-flowing lowland ditches may support dense patches of starwort (*Callitriche verna*) in summer, its weak stems bearing tiny, inconspicuous green flowers.

Below *Epilobium roseum* is one of the smaller-flowered willowherbs, growing in localized patches on river banks and in other damp places, such as roadside ditches.

Elodea canadensis spreads with its upright stems very closely packed together. The result is a mixed blessing: in the canopy area, where the shoots are young and active, abundant oxygen is produced, but beneath, in the dark conditions around the straggling leafless stems, wholly deoxygenated conditions are encouraged – a smelly blackness in which nothing other than bacteria can survive.

By contrast, such rooting plants as starwort (*Callitriche*), hornwort (*Ceratophyllum*) and the water millfoils (*Myriophyllum*), which are much more open in their pattern of growth, are physiologically kinder, because light and well-oxygenated conditions persist amongst the stems, right down to the surface of the mud itself.

To a degree, marsh plants invade hedgerow ditches which, because of the shading from the hedge and the tendency to collect water, are frequently damp for much of the year, and may turn into small streams during wet weather. As a result, you may find that plants such as water hemlock (*Cicuta*), purple loosestrife (*Lythrum*), willowherbs (*Epilobium*) and meadowsweet (*Spiraea*) dominate a ditch, while normal meadow plants are growing a few feet away.

SALTMARSHES

Saltmarshes provide a contrasting environment, because they are conditioned by the presence of salt. Saltmarsh occurs in estuaries and on flat low-lying ground close to tidal rivers.

Salt is deposited in the soil when the sea floods the area at extreme high tides. Sea water also enters the ground through natural seepage. The soil tends to be poorly aerated and in hot spells of weather, when the ground dries out, the concentrations of salt can become very high. Few plants can tolerate these severe physiological conditions. Those which can survive in this environment must possess adaptations to help them cope, not only with high salt concentration, but also, curiously, with the opposite extreme, because in a period of short tides and persistent heavy rain, the salt can be leached out of the soil.

Saltmarsh plants

Plants living in a saltmarsh are described as *halophytes* and, in many respects, the modifications that they show are similar to those of *xerophytes*, plants able to tolerate very dry conditions (see p125). This is because the high concentration of salt in marshes permeated by sea water is physiologically drying. If salt spray lands on the leaves of a normal plant, sap will be drawn out through the process of osmosis, since the concentration of salts is stronger outside than inside the tissues. To counter this potentially life-threatening condition, halophytes typically develop fleshy leaves that can store large amounts of water, and the leaf surfaces possess waxy coverings to reduce transpiration. Some are covered with short hairs, assisting water retention. The group of plants known as glassworts (*Salicornia* spp) are worth looking for. Among other saltmarsh plants the grass, sea poa (*Glyceria maritima*), is one of the commonest.

Left Alder bog is one of the most advanced stages before water habitat reverts to normal dry land.

SAND DUNES

Sand dune plants suffer similar physiological effects from high salt content in the air, but dunes possess their own peculiarities, one of which is that they are subject to intense illumination and often become very hot. On the other hand, sand is very well drained and therefore tends to be spared any appreciable build-up of salt in soil water.

Another important feature of sand is that it is extremely mobile and, when dry, the grains are blown about freely. If they meet an obstacle they begin to congregate into what may eventually form a mound or dune, a mobile structure that is constantly being eroded on the windward side, and increasing on the leeward. Should the obstruction be a plant without any special ability to cope, it will, in the normal course of events, be engulfed. Dune plants, however, have developed their own strategies to counter the uncertain mobility of their bed. They benefit from extensive anchoring systems, and by constant growth they keep their "heads" above any sand accumulation.

Grasses

Grasses are vital to the development of sand dunes. Sea couch grasses (*Agropyron junceum* and *A. pungens*) are often the first to establish a hold in young dunes. Both can tolerate temporary immersion in sea water

Above *Halimione portulacoides*, the sea purslane, is a typical halophyte plant, inhabiting saltmarshes and the edges of creek beds. The fleshy leaves store water to combat the physiological drying effect of salt.

Left Shingle beaches support their own brand of flora. The sea kale (*Crambe maritima*), the leaves of which are dark green, thick and crinkly, is one of the forerunners of the domestic cabbage.

and both rely on vigorous creeping rootstocks to build up a resilient mesh. Once established with the pioneering species, the dune supports marram grass (*Ammophila arenaria*) on its higher ramparts, though marram will not tolerate immersion. Where a dune is particularly exposed to wind, a third species, sea lyme grass (*Elymus arenarius*), often appears before marram.

One of the most distinctive features of these grasses, other than their extensive rooting systems, lies in the way their leaves are inrolled at the edges to reduce transpiration. This defence mechanism is assisted by the growth of hairs on the leaf surface. If you cut a section of *Ammophila* leaf blade and examine it under the lens, you will observe that the convex outer surface is smooth, with a thick cuticle and no transpiration pores, but the inner surface is folded into convolutions, on the tips of which are stiff bristles and thick cuticle. In the hollows, where the cuticle is thin, are the pores or *stomata* through which the plant breathes. The effect is to offer a heavily-protected surface area for transpiration. It is interesting to compare the different types of the grass *Agropyron*, which grows both inland and by the sea – the sea shore species (*A. pungens* and *A. junceum*) are closely related to inland couch grass (*A. repens*), but while the sand dune forms have leaves with inrolled edges, couch has flattened leaf blades.

Below The most common grass of sand dunes, *Elymus farctus*, or sea couch grass, relies on vigorous creeping rootstocks to build a firm anchor in the shifting sand.

Right Sand dunes are hot and dry and provide little support for rooting systems. Only plants with the most effective of adaptations can cope with such habitats.

Other sea shore plants

Once established, the dune will become colonized by other plants, including sea holly (*Eryngium maritimum*), sand sedge (*Carex arenaria*) and sea purslane (*Halimione portulacoides*), but invariably the first shrub to appear will be tamarisk (*Tamarix*).

Shingle beaches develop their own flora – look out for the flat spreading plants of sea kale (*Crambe maritima*), which is, incidentally, the forerunner of the edible cabbage, the lilac-flowered sea rocket (*Cakile maritima*) and the yellow horned poppy (*Glaucum flavum*).

The plants mentioned are merely among the more common illustrations of sea shore flora. All, however, tend to show common features: either reduced foliage, or tough, thick, water-retaining leaves, which often possess a bluish or glaucous bloom and a waxy feel.

Shrubs such as tamarisk compensate for salt attack by having leaves that are reduced to minute overlapping flaps, extending into feathery fronds.

CLIFFS AND ROCKS

Sea cliffs and rocky areas above the high water mark are also physiologically dry places, conditioned by salt spray and almost constant wind action. The soil is often very shallow, with a high humus content, and subject to the same intense illumination as the fore-shore. The plants, though, do not have to cope with shifting soil, nor with salt in the ground water, so they tend to develop shallower spreading root systems, flat, cushion-like rosettes of foliage and short flowering stems. They include sea pink (*Statice maritima*), sea campion (*Silene maritima*), sea lavender (*Limonium vulgare*) and rock samphire (*Crithmum maritimum*).

Many of these plants are halophytes and will also carpet salt marshes. They have developed the familiar thick fleshy leaves with reduced surface area to counter the water loss due to the osmotic action of salt. Bare rocks also become covered with lichen patches, one of the most commonly-found species being the yellow crusted lichen (*Xanthoria parietina*).

Above Sea pink (*Armeria maritima*) bears reduced and rather fleshy leaves to combat both physical and physiological drought conditions on an exposed cliff face.

Below Sea cliffs, frequently unaffected by agricultural sprays or ploughing, provide a glorious array of flowers specially adapted to cope with exposure to wind and salt spray.

VERGES

Because of the regular use of de-icing salts on motorways and other major roads, rock salt accumulates in the gravelly soil adjacent to the hard shoulder, and one interesting result is that as the motorway verge area matures, so halophytes begin to establish themselves, often hundreds of miles from the coast. Watch out for salt-marsh plants living far from their accustomed habitat as you travel the highways of Europe, but not, of course, if you are doing the driving!

Below The verges of motorways and other arterial roads often remain untouched, apart from an occasional mowing close to the hard shoulder, and are an unexpected haven for wild flowers.

Above The yellow lichen *Xanthoria parietina* frequently encrusts exposed rock and stone faces. One of the pioneer plants, it extends down as far as the splash zone of high water.

Below The sea lyme grass (*Elymus*) is particularly adept at coping with exposure and is typically the first grass species to appear on young, developing dunes.

MOUNTAINS, MOORLANDS AND DOWNLANDS
INTRODUCTION

High ground offers a number of peculiar growing conditions, and the plants that inhabit such elevated regions are adapted accordingly. Although the title of this chapter implies three different situations, all are mountain environments of one form or another.

Rugged "young" mountains are characterized by high pastures, with much exposed sharp rock, tumbling water torrents, frequent movement of surface stone, and readily eroded patches of soil. The ground surface is at the mercy of wind, water and ice.

As youthful mountains age and mellow, the sharp edges disappear and the eroded humps become clothed with a layer of peat, which may eventually extend to a depth of 10 metres or more in certain boggy areas. Peat is raw humus – vegetable remains that are subject to little or no decay. This is because the ground is often waterlogged and contains none of the earthworms or bacteria that are responsible for rotting, and mean temperatures in such locations are generally too low to allow for effective decomposition.

Mountains such as the Cairngorms of northern Scotland, and the French Alps, though resting in a temperate climatic zone, are effectively extensions of the Arctic. The result can be a high, acid moorland, as distinct from lowland moor or fen, which is generally much more neutral or even alkaline, because the ground water in these lower regions contains a high percentage of soluble salts. Acid moorland does not generally extend above 1000 metres, and its flora is accountably different from that of a mountain pasture.

If the mountain is soft and alkaline, as is the case with those constructed from chalk and limestone, the erosion of the virgin rock is very rapid and the mountains reduce to low humps. A shallow soil, sometimes measuring only a few centimetres, is produced from the accumulated plant debris. Such soil is often poor in salts, because most of the calcium carbonate content is dissolved through the action of rain, which contains carbon dioxide and is therefore slightly acid in its action. The effect of this is that the soil becomes leached of mineral salts. Beech woodlands often develop on chalk and limestone hills, and if the trees are cut down, resulting in grassy hill pastures, the habitat becomes known as downland.

Left "Young" mountains appear rugged, with a good deal of exposed rock and movement of stone at the surface. They are frequently punctured by water torrents, which assist the erosion.

Upland habitats

All the upland habitats suffer from disadvantages in terms of living space. Exposure is a major factor. Trees will only survive up to a certain altitude, known as the tree line, and above this little shelter is afforded from the wind. Furthermore, because of the way air currents are stimulated in relation to the contours of the land, mountain regions are almost always windy. Typically, they are associated with strong updraughts, and as the altitude increases, so the temperature drops proportionally, with the result that the temperature at the base of an alpine valley may be between 20 and 30°F warmer than that on the peak. This produces a gradation of flora, from arctic to temperate species, within a very small survey area. The soil may be both poor in nutrients and shallow; often it consists of little more than a thin layer of peat, and this, although composed almost entirely of organic material, possesses virtually no readily-available nutrients. On slopes, soluble salts tend to be leached out and washed down into the valleys. High ground, because of the action of wind and lack of water-retaining soil, can also be physiologically very dry. Conversely, the slopes of mountains facing prevailing weather, such as those along the Atlantic Coastal areas, are regularly drenched with rain. An additional hazard faced by cushion plants, which constitute the bulk of species growing on high ground, can come from certain species of birds, which will tear apart softer foliage in the spring months, and use it to line their nests.

Above As mountains age and mature, they become more rounded in profile and are often clothed with deep layers of peat. In this condition, they are termed high moorlands.

Below Acid moorlands, typically subject to high levels of rainfall, are clothed largely with common cotton grass (*Eriophorum polystachion*), which develops as dense tussocks bearing cottony white inflorescences.

ALPINE ADAPTATIONS

The object of this chapter is to look at plants growing in a range of upland habitats. By definition, however, alpines are strictly those species that live in high pastures, soil pockets and rock fissures above the tree line. One of the first limitations to become apparent when you study mountain plants is that the short growing season and the closed nature of the community do not encourage annuals. Many mountain habitats are ice-bound for nine months of the year, and although the snow protects plants from the worst ravages of winter weather, the opportunity to photosynthesize, flower and set seed may be limited to a few weeks between June and August. Almost all species thus come within the category of hardy perennials, able to cope with fluctuating extremes.

The plants, whether they be trees, bushes or small herbaceous species, are all equipped to meet the challenges of living at higher altitudes. Generally, such plants are small and stunted; few possess tall stems, which would be vulnerable to wind action, and all are modified to cope with the drying action of wind and frost.

Above *Silene vulgaris*, the white bladder campion, is a tallish, erect plant, typical of lowland fields and waste places, although there are smaller upland forms.

Left Trees in exposed upland locations are usually characterized by stunted growth and varying degrees of trunk and branch distortion. Often, they grow at an angle, bending over with the prevailing wind.

In addition, many have to meet the conflicting problems of having their roots in waterlogged soil and their green, above-ground parts subject to very rapid water loss through evaporation. As a rule, alpine plants do not exceed 15cm in height, and cushioning is the most typical form. This has a number of advantages: since the stems are tightly bunched together, they offer a smooth overall profile against the wind, and water loss is minimized because the exposed surface area of each plant is very restricted.

You will often observe markedly different characteristics between related species, one of which lives in a mountain habitat, while the other is a lowland plant. In lowland areas, the white bladder campion (*Silene vulgaris*) develops into a handsome upright plant; where species such as sea campion (*S. maritima*) occur in an alpine situation, the plant is very low-growing, with smaller, thicker leaves and an increased number of non-flowering shoots.

Many of the prettier alpine plants – curiously, these often bear colourful flowers in spite of the lack of pollinating insects at high altitudes – are familiar to gardeners because they are grown in rockeries. The *Campanula* family are amongst the most attractive. Spread all over the northern hemisphere, they include many garden hybrids. One of the commonest of the wild species is the harebell (*C. rotundifolia*), and if you examine one of these you will notice that it has two distinct types of leaves. Where the risk of evaporation is less, at the base, the leaves are heart-shaped, but those on the stems are much narrower, offering a reduced surface area to the wind.

Below The saxifrages (*Saxifraga*) are typical of plants with an alpine habit. They develop as compact cushions of growth, which effectively resist wind action and drying.

Right By way of contrast with *Silene vulgaris*, the related species of sea campion (*Silene maritima*) is a typically low-growing alpine adaptation.

Above Harebells (*Campanula rotundifolia*) are among the prettiest and most delicate of alpine flowers. The plant produces two distinct leaf types in an adaptation against the drying action of wind.

The saxifrages (*Saxifraga*) are predominantly mountain plants, as are cushion pinks (*Silene*), gentians (*Gentiana*) and houseleeks (*Sempervirum*), and most of them possess small tough leaves. Many of the Compositae which grow at altitudes, including the famous edelweiss (*Leontopodium*), protect themselves against dehydration by growing dense woolly hairs all over the exposed surfaces of leaves and stems. *Sempervirum*, by contrast, is wholly hairless (*glabrous*) but its leaves are fleshy water-storage tanks with leathery surfaces that reduce transpiration loss.

MOORLANDS

European moorlands fall into two distinct types – cotton grass moors and heather moors – although there are many intermediate stages between the two. Most exist where once there was woodland.

Cotton grass moors are formed of very deep and soggy acid peat. The material lacks mineral salts and has a very high organic content, made up of the remains of previous generations of moorland plants. Were one to dig down through the layers of peat, one would eventually come across remnants, right at the bottom, of trees such as birch and hazel. Moorlands of this type tend to be subject to high levels of rainfall – 100cm or more per annum – and they consist almost entirely of broad stretches of cotton grass (*Eriophorum*). Cotton grass develops into dense tussocks, and progresses by creeping underground stems. The leaves are mostly at the base of the plant and are invariably back-rolled, to protect their transpiring surfaces. The flowering stems are about 30cm high, and the cotton effect is created by slender bristles, which protrude perhaps 2 or 3cm from the terminal umbels as the inflorescence ripens.

Where the ground is particularly saturated, patches of bog moss (*Sphagnum* species) may appear, together with soft rush (*Juncus effusus*), but in general cotton grass moor is too wet to support many other plants. In drier spots, crowberry (*Vaccinium vitis-idaea*) and bilberry (*V. myrtillus*) may appear among hair grasses

(*Aira* species). Very few wild flowers populate cotton grass moors, one of the more common being the small species of Northern rock cress (*Arabis petraea*) decked in high summer with small white blooms. Where the slopes become steep and better drained, stretches of bracken (*Pteridium aquilinum*) can also develop.

Heather moors

Heather moors are richer in species and tend to be prettier-looking, particularly towards the later part of the year, when they take on a rich purple colouring. In contrast to the wet and deep peat of the cotton grass moor, the soil of a heather moor is shallower and better drained. It is still acidic, but a typical heather moor is sandy. Although the bedrock of sandstone is

Left Cotton grass moors provide a peculiar environment, consisting of very deep acidic peat. This lacks mineral salts, but is very high in organic material, and as a result the rhizomes of the grass penetrate vigorously to clothe large areas.

Left The cotton grass inflorescence gains its usual appearance because of the hypogynous bristles, which protrude far beyond the glumes to form tufts that are silky or cottony white.

Right Furze or gorse (*Ulex europaeus*) is one of the commoner xerophytic shrubs on heaths, and sandy and stony wastelands in western Europe though it does not occur around the Mediterranean region. Its distinctive flowers appear all year.

Below Northern rock cress (*Arabis petraea*) is a small perennial flower which extends through mountainous regions of northern Europe. Its small white flowers can easily be overlooked.

more common, heather moors can also develop on limestone, and in each case the surface layers become independent of the chemical nature of the foundation.

The main flowering plant is ling (*Calluna vulgaris*), but the habitat also supports heathers such as bell heather (*Erica cinerea*), common in western Europe, and Mediterranean heather (*E. carnea*), which is more typically found on the lower slopes of mountains stretching across from the Swiss Alps to the Balkans. Other members of the Ericaceae family, including bilberry, whortleberry and cranberry (*Myrtillus* species), as well as cloudberry (*Rubus chamaemorus*) which belongs to the rose family, also thrive on heather moors.

Gorse (*Ulex*) is a familiar plant of mountain regions, showing extreme adaptation to life in a dry habitat. There are two European species, *U. europaeus* and *U. minor*. Both are found in western Europe, and *U. europaeus* also occurs in central Europe, though neither are of Mediterranean distribution.

CHALK DOWNS

Where limestone has erupted into hills, it offers conditions that are different in some respects to those prevailing on mountains and moorlands which have a bedrock of granite, sandstone or shale. One of the softest and purest forms of limestone is chalk; this weathers rapidly, is alkaline in chemistry, possesses numerous fissures, and is highly porous. Because of its softness, a wider variety of plants can gain a purchase, and as these rot away, a layer of humus accumulates. Any potential acidity, however, is countered by the chalk, so that worms and bacteria of decomposition thrive, and the resulting soil is thin but crumbly, and is naturally balanced.

The stability of chalk downs is highly dependent on the grasses that become established on them. These plants develop thick interlacing tangles of roots which

Left Among the taller aromatic herbs of chalk and limestone uplands, marjoram (*Origanum vulgare*) bears pale mauve flowers on an erect tough downy stem which, like other members of the Labiatae, is square in section. The northern European species is annual while the sweet marjoram of the Mediterranean regions is perennial.

Above Wild thyme (*Thymus drucei*) is common on chalk downlands, where it grows in low tufted rosettes of small leaves and massed purplish flowers. It flowers throughout the summer months, and its distinctive aroma is produced by special oil glands in the leaves.

penetrate the chalk and effectively hold the soil to the rock. Without the plant covering, the soil layer washes away rapidly, but within the mesh of grasses, all of which are typically short, fine-leaved forms, a wide range of rosette or small-leaved upland plants can thrive. Here, the number of species is far in excess of anything that a more acid moorland can support. Roughly speaking, if it is not adversely influenced by man, a good chalk grassland will contain as many as 50 species in a square metre.

A major problem, however, is that chalk downlands, particularly in southern England but also in other parts of Europe, have been exploited for crop growing, and this can reduce the number of wildflower species down to less than 10.

One of the commonest of the hardier species is the aromatic wild thyme (*Thymus drucei*), which shows all the familiar adaptations – a low profile, a tendency to form a cushion, together with short flowering stems and tiny leaves. Amongst the taller Labiatae, marjoram (*Origanum vulgare*) is a tufted downy annual bearing pale mauve flowers, and wild basil (*Clinopodium vulgare*) also frequents chalk hills, as does meadow sage (*Salvia pratensis*).

Among the Rosaceae, wild strawberry (*Fragaria vesca*) is one of the more common rosette plants, while the taller salad burnet (*Poterium sanguisorba*), which bears small leaflets and petalless, globular flower heads, also favours dry chalk.

Keep an eye out on downlands for some of the wild relatives of our familiar edible umbellifers, including wild carrot (*Daucus carota*) and wild parsnip (*Pastanica sativa*). Both favour dry chalk and limestone. *Daucus* is the only common umbellifer bearing white flowers; the lower bracts that fringe the umbels are 3-forked, and if you look closely at the head you will usually find a single red flower right in the centre, and you will notice that the umbel becomes concave as it matures. *Pastanica* is hairy, with simple pinnate leaves; it smells strongly of parsnip when rubbed, and bears yellow umbels.

Cowslip (*Primula*) is one of the prettier common yellow flowers of spring downlands. Among those that

Left *Primula veris*, the cowslip, is designed to cope with meadow grass growing around it in the spring. Its leaves are basal but the flowers are borne on long, leafless peduncles.

Above Several species of umbellifers are common on downlands, including the wild parsnip (*Pastanica sativa*). The forerunner of the domestic vegetable, its glands secrete an aromatic oil.

appear later in the summer are lady's bedstraw (*Galium verum*) and weld (*Reseda lutea*). The vetches are also well represented on chalk and limestone hills, as are a number of the Orchidaceae, including pyramidal (*Anacamptis*), common spotted (*Dactylorchis*) and bee (*Ophrys*) orchids.

CHALK AND LIMESTONE HILLS

Among the shrubs that grow on limestone uplands, gorse (*Ulex*), genista (*Genista*) and broom (*Cytisus*) – all members of the peaflower family – are particularly adapted to the dry well-drained conditions. Cotoneaster (*Cotoneaster*) is found extensively, though sometimes the plants are cultivated hybrid escapes. Whitebeam (*Sorbus aria*) and privet (*Ligustrum*) are also common, the former being a small tree bearing leaves with distinctive silvery undersurfaces, dense umbels of small creamy white flowers and red berries. Privet – a more or less evergreen shrub, but with tough, well-cuticled leaves – develops attractive panicles of pure white flowers and, when ripe, shiny black berries. Juniper (*Juniperus*) is the most frequent of the

Below Privet (*Ligustrum vulgare*) is well adapted for life on dry chalk uplands. Its leaves are tough with thick resistant cuticles.

Above Cotoneaster often grows wild as a hybridized garden escape. The shrub, best known for its brilliant red berries, is adapted to dry, well-drained upland conditions, and has small tough leaves that resist transpiration.

Below Yew (*Taxus baccata*) is one of the more typical coniferous trees on limestone and chalk hills. The flowers are dioecious, very small male catkins being borne in the leaf axils, and the fruits contained in bright red juicy cups.

evergreen shrubby conifers, and yew (*Taxus*) also favours limestone and chalk hills. Among the deciduous trees, hawthorn (*Crataegus*), elder (*Sambucus*) and beech (*Fagus*) are the most common, though sycamore (*Acer*) and ash (*Fraxinus*) appear regularly.

XEROPHYTES

Many of the plants discussed in this chapter are *xerophytes* – species adapted for life in habitats that may be physically or physiologically dry. In addition to high ground areas, xerophytes also occur on sand dunes, cliffs, limestone "pavements", and other habitats that offer locally arid conditions. Essentially, they are adopted to retain as much water as is possible within the plant, and to reduce water loss through transpiration to a minimum, and the practical botanist should be able to recognize different xerophytic modifications.

All plants have their surfaces clothed with a layer of skin-like cells known as the *epidermis*. On their exposed outer margins the cells can secrete an semi-impervious coating, the *cuticle*, which is continuous over the whole surface, except at the transpiration pores or *stomata*. In hydrophytes – aquatic plants – the cuticle is thin or non-existent and the transfer of materials goes on all over the surface of stems and leaves, but at the other end of the environmental scale, xerophyte cuticle is often massively thickened and may also be backed up by a layer of totally waterproof wax. Stomata are reduced or specially guarded.

As a simple experiment, take any ordinary leaf with an obvious upper and lower surface, such as a leaf from an apple or pear tree, and coat the upper surface with petroleum jelly. Do the same for another leaf from the same plant, but this time apply the coating to the under surface, then hang both leaves in a dry place. Bear in mind, incidentally, that transpiration takes place during the day and ceases at night. The example which has been coated on its under surface will stay fresh for much longer than the other, because in such a bifacial leaf most of the stomata are located on the underside. With a leaf such as a holly (*Ilex*), in which the contrast between the two surfaces is even more pronounced, the upper surface being protected by a very tough, shiny cuticle, you will be able to maintain the freshness for a considerable period, simply by coating the under surface.

In a xerophyte, the stomatal surface is always heavily protected. Often, the leaf curls in the plane of its midrib. The leaves of grasses and sedges, which have similar surfaces on both the top and bottom, tend to be up-rolled, and stomata are absent from the lower surfaces; in heathers and other plants, which have stomata on the lower surface only, the leaves are back-rolled. In all cases, the stomata are sunk into grooves or pits.

Above Mistletoe (*Viscum album*) is a parasitic evergreen that grows on the branches of several trees. It shows some xerophytic modification in its thick semi-succulent leaves.

Below Gorse (*Ulex*) is a woody shrub with numerous short branches that end in sharp thorns. Most of the leaves are also reduced to thorns making the plant highly efficient at living in dry habitats.

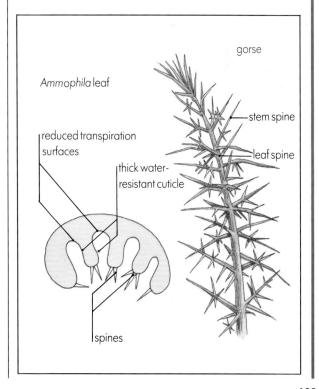

gorse

Ammophila leaf

reduced transpiration surfaces

thick water-resistant cuticle

stem spine

leaf spine

spines

Left A frequent adaptation of xerophytes, seen in the broom (*Cytisus scoparius*), is a reduction in leaf size, but the broom goes one step further, shedding its leaves during periods of drought. It compensates for the loss of photosynthetic tissue in its leaves by increasing the surface area of its stems.

Equally concealed from the casual observer is the mechanical ability of many xerophytic leaves to roll up or flatten out, a device which is important because it enables the plant to transpire as well as to retain moisture. At the base of the grooves are thin-walled cells known as *hinge cells*, which lose water more quickly than the rest. As they contract, they draw the sides of the hinge together and the leaf rolls up. Conversely, as soon as the hinge cells fill with water again, the leaf blade flattens.

Many xerophytic plants are covered with hairs, and these also assist with the retention of water, because they act as a blanket, trapping moist air next to the epidermal surface. The field senecio (*S. campestris*), which is a frequent mountain and downland plant, and some of the Labiatae, which occur in dry places, are amongst the commoner examples of plants with leaves guarded in this way.

Water loss is minimized in xerophytes by reducing the overall size of the leaves, and by adjusting from a typical broad flat shape to a thin linear profile. The leaves of ling (*Calluna*) or thyme (*Thymus*) demonstrate this well.

Sometimes, as is the case with gorse (*Ulex*), the reduction goes so far as to result in a leaf vestige in the form of a spine. Broom (*Cytisus*) actually sheds its already-small leaves during the dry season. Serious leaf reduction or loss immediately runs the plant into another problem, because reduction of the transpiration area also cuts down that available for photosynthesis. To compensate, the stems of xerophytes such as *Ulex* and *Cytisus* become highly photosynthetic and increase their area by developing longitudinal ridges.

An increase in the fleshiness of organs is another xerophytic modification. This reaches its most extreme form in the cacti, but *Sempervivum* and *Sedum* species frequently develop fleshy, rubbery leaves which act as water storage organs.

Above One of the most popular cultivated heathers, the Mediterranean heather (*Erica carnea*) offers cultivars with a variety of flower colours. Notice how the tiny leaves, appearing in whorls, are rolled back on their edges.

Left Ling (*Calluna vulgaris*) is the most commonly distributed of the heaths. Reaching, when mature, almost a metre tall, its leaves are very small and tough to combat excessive transpiration, and its small pink flowers are borne in the leaf axils.

127

URBAN BOTANY
INTRODUCTION

The process of changing the natural countryside of Europe into a thoroughly *unnatural* landscape probably began more than five thousand years ago as the virgin forests were cut down. The agricultural revolution played a major part in shaping the woods and fields we know today, but it was the massive expansion of industry towards the end of the 18th century, coupled with the exploitation of iron and coal, which created the most extreme form of artificial habitat – the aptly-named "concrete jungle". Nowhere has man exploited the natural environment for his own ends more than in the development of towns and cities.

"What man proposes, God disposes", and the speed at which nature will take over an urban area if left to its own devices is sobering. Perversely, such habitats,

Below The hogweed (*Heracleum sphondylium*) is a rugged perennial, inhabiting urban areas. Like many opportunist plants, it has the ability to produce flowering stems, bloom, and set seed rapidly. The roots are tough and resistant to all but the most determined attack.

even when controlled efficiently, often provide a richer variety of plant species than a piece of remote, unspoilt countryside. Seen from the air, a major European conurbation is full of greenery; inevitably, the suburbs are richer in terms of nature, but roads are frequently lined with trees and fringed with grassy verges right into a city centre. Railway embankments penetrate with their own brand of jungle, and there are large areas of maintained inner city park, cemeteries, and urban golf courses. Blocks of flats are surrounded by greenery, and most houses possess gardens of some form or another. In addition, there are always the more ephemeral patches of waste ground. Surprisingly, perhaps, an average-sized European city will often support in excess of a million trees within its boundaries, at a density per hectare greater than that in the surrounding countryside.

Gardening tastes vary across Europe, the English and the Dutch probably leading the field in terms of enthusiasm. Scandinavians tend not to be keen gardeners because of the low temperatures; German gardens are generally formal; French utilitarian, and their Mediterranean counterparts are colourful but tend to contain only a limited number of species, probably due to the difficulties of watering in hot dry areas.

The urban dilemma

Wherever it emerges, the flora of urban areas is faced with a real "Catch 22" situation: buildings provide shelter and offer abundant climbing frames, but they also cover much ground impenetrably; street lighting provides artificial illumination, while the buildings shut out considerable amounts of daylight. The air is often several degrees warmer in a big city, yet it is polluted with such noxious gases as carbon monoxide, sulphur dioxide and hydrogen sulphide. The soil may be richer in nutrients, offering a range of types from

Left Yellow alyssum (*Alyssum saxatile*) is an evergreen perennial shrub modified to grow in dry rocky places. The narrow pointed leaves appear greyish with a fine coating of downy hairs which act as an evaporation barrier.

Right The flowers of deadly nightshade, a member of the Solanaceae family, are borne on arching stems. The corolla is large, nearly 2cm long and a dull purplish blue. The berries that follow are shiny black "lozenges".

Below The henbane (*Hyoscyamus niger*) is another member of the Solanaceae with strong historical associations, having been grown for its narcotic properties.

allotment loam to power station ash heaps, but it is frequently contaminated with industrial by-products. Open ground often becomes available to opportunistic plants through demolition and in many cases it will have been conveniently loosened by earthmovers, but it may just as quickly be concreted over again.

Many of the plants that inhabit urban areas are geared to take advantage of opportunities instantly, as and when they arise. Such species may produce seeds that possess great vitality, able to remain dormant over long periods of time. Once germinated, they put down aggressive rooting systems and flower in the space of a week or so, sometimes even in a matter of days and many are particularly resistant to pollutants in the air and in the soil.

A high proportion of the species will be introductions. Some exotics will have arrived casually on ships, shoes and the wheels of vehicles. Others will have naturalized as escapes from suburban gardens, or from town parks, which are often planted with specimens originating in parts of the world far from Europe. A great deal of fascination also lies in the historical associations of plants such as deadly nightshade (*Atropa*), evening primrose (*Oenothera*) and henbane (*Hyoscyamus*).

CHARTING URBAN BOTANY

The principles are similar to those applied to a woodland or a field, but urban botany will be influenced much more strongly by related factors such as pollution, and will show considerable localized variance even over short distances.

Let us assume that you have decided to survey a patch of derelict waste ground. The first task is to visit the local library in order to discover the history of the place. When was the land first built on? What was there before? Why did it subsequently become derelict and when? What, if anything, has been dumped there since. This background information is all-important because it may have a major influence in determining which plants will grow on the site.

Next, check carefully *over the whole area*, to assess the soil types. In a pasture or meadow, you may fairly safely assume a consistent soil, but this is not so in an urban environment. Ash or clinker may have been dumped at a certain point, or there may be high values of brick rubble in some parts and not others. Some other form of hard core, related to a past use of the site, may have been deposited, and it is not uncommon to find a spreading of chalk or limestone, introduced by man, over a natural clay base. You will need to take various samples to identify the nature of the soil and its pH (see p.140). Now examine what is currently being done with the site; for example, are people depositing garden or domestic rubbish there? You must also check for other factors, such as high buildings, adjacent industry or outfalls, that may affect the area.

All the information must be incorporated into the ground plan of the area because it will have influenced the botany. It is ideal to chart an urban site over a period of not less than 12 months, though longer-term surveys may reveal far more than you would be likely to find in a more stable, rural location, because an urban "jungle" is probably changing far more rapidly than its country counterpart. The frequency of survey through a calendar year will be dictated by the amount of time you have available, but it should include not less than four seasonal visits. Any alterations to the site between inspections are extremely important and must be noted.

Add any other relevant information. Footpaths or animal tracks, for example, are particularly important, because many plant seeds are spread on feet and clothing. It is worth taking temperature readings and, if possible, comparing these with similar records from a site just out of town, because the climate within an urban area will normally be a little milder, and this may affect time of flowering and size of plants.

Plant categories

When you are ready to add plant species, a number of distinctions need to be made:

1 Perennial plants that are "endemic" to the urban jungle
2 Plants that have entered as short-term opportunists
3 Garden hybrids that have become naturalized
4 Tree and shrub species that are perhaps outside their normal range, but have been introduced artificially
5 Other plants that have been introduced historically for a specific purpose; for example, for medicinal value
6 Exotic aliens that have become established – this may be particularly interesting in a location adjacent to docks or beside a railway.

All these should be distinguished on the chart by a system of colour coding, so you will not only have species in relation to soil peculiarities but also classified according to their origins and their use by man. One trait that may be revealed is that plant species which are rare in the wild are much more prolific on urban ground. Look for some typical examples: the hellebores, *H. viridis*, for example, grow in very localized sites on limestone, but are frequently cultivated. Himalayan balsam (*Impatiens glandulifera*) is a similar case. Mezereon (*Daphne mezereum*) and box (*Buxus sempervirens*) may be infrequent shrubs in the wild, but because of their ornamental popularity they are comparatively common on urban waste ground.

Pollution indicators

One important exercise you can carry out relates to urban pollution. Lichens, as we have seen, are very accurate pollution indicators. Note carefully the species – if any – which are occurring. If the survey is to extend over several years, you may notice trends upwards or downwards in lichen frequency. There is, however, a more subtle investigative technique to establish whether any of the more common wild plants are affected by pollution. You may select

Basic soil type: heavy clay

dilapidated low brick wall

ash heap

high wall (brick)

area of brick rubble

Left To chart an urban habitat, you will need to adopt much the same principles as for any rural site, although an urban environment is likely to be influenced more strongly by factors such as pollution and the varying make-up of the soil.

1 Oxford ragwort
2 Stinging nettle
3 Rosebay willowherb
4 Buddleia bushes
5 Red campion
6 Elder
7 Bramble
8 Wild flowering peas and vetches
9 Lichens

rosebay willow herb (*Epilobium angustifolium*), stinging nettle (*Urtica dioica*) or ox-eye daisy (*Chrysanthemum leucanthemum*), all of which are widespread plants, and therefore suitable for this purpose. Make a careful study of the plants of the chosen species that are to be found in your urban jungle, taking note of leaf size, numbers of leaves, markings, height at flowering, size of flowers, flower markings and variations. This information can be compared against samples of the same species growing in a rural location.

OPPORTUNISTIC ANNUALS

It is important to distinguish between the opportunist annuals, which work on the basis of speed, and the perennials, which rely on tough invasive rootstocks. Ragworts (*Senecio*) are amongst the most robust and aggressive of the annuals commonly found in urban areas. Once the seeds have germinated, they produce a vigorous tangled rooting system, and if you try pulling up a ragwort you will find that unless the soil has been loosened the stem will invariably break off, leaving the rooting system to generate a new flowering shoot. The plants mature to flowering within a matter of days, and some of them, including groundsel (*S. vulgaris*), produce seed more or less all the year round.

Other ragworts have spread by very precise routes. The so-called Oxford ragwort (*S. squalidus*) is native to

Left *Senecio jacobaea*, the common ragwort, is an opportunist plant, growing from a perennial rootstock with stems that reach a metre in height. The attractive, bright yellow flowers are borne in compact terminal corymb heads.

Above Black nightshade (*Solanum nigrum*) is an annual opportunist member of the Solanaceae which will quickly invade disturbed ground or bare soil.

the Mediterranean region and favours limestone soils, but it is also prevalent on the volcanic slopes of mount Etna in Sicily. In the late 18th century it was introduced to the Botanic Gardens at Oxford in England as an unusual plant, but because it thrives on burnt ground it has spread rapidly, as an escape, along railway tracks as far north as Scotland, and now it can be found all over Europe.

Another very widespread annual weed which

quickly colonizes disturbed ground is black night-shade (*Solanum nigrum*). Related to the potato, it bears small white flowers followed by distinctive berries. In continental Europe, these ripen from green to yellow or dingy red, but in southern Britain they turn black.

In southern Europe, the thorn apple (*Datura stramonium*), which belongs to the same Solanaceae family as *S. nigrum*, is a pernicious annual of roadsides and waste ground, but it has spread across Europe as far north as southern England. It often appears on cultivated ground and is easily recognized by its holly-shaped leaves, the large, trumpet-shaped, whitish flowers, and its even more striking fruits, with their wrinkled black seeds. The spread of *Datura* has been assisted through its bygone popularity as a medicinal plant, and also by the vitality of its seed, which can remain dormant but viable for many years.

Other examples of annuals which have invaded urban areas from the countryside are fat hen (*Chenopodium album*), red poppy (*Papaver rhoeas*), shepherd's purse (*Capsella bursa-pastoris*) and chickweed (*Stellaria media*).

Below Groundsel (*Senecio vulgaris*) is one of the commonest weeds of cultivation throughout much of Europe. It relies on year-round flowering, and the rapid production and setting of numerous seeds.

Top and **above** Among the more pernicious plants of waste ground, the thorn apple (*Datura stramonium*) has spread across Europe as far as southern England. It produces attractive trumpet-shaped flowers, followed by the striking fruits (berries) that provide its common name.

URBAN PERENNIALS

Among the perennials that have successfully colonized the urban landscape, one of the first to appear in spring is coltsfoot (*Tussilago farfara*). A member of the Compositae family, looking not unlike an unseasonal dandelion, coltsfoot favours bare clay soils. It spreads by creeping rootstocks and produces large hoof-shaped leaves, the solitary flower heads being borne on upright scaly shoots.

If winners in the urban jungle need to move fast and invade whatever living space is available, the large bindweed (*Convolvulus sepium*), with its fragile, showy, pristine white blooms, and the smaller bindweeds, such as *C. minor* and *C. arvensis*, are excellent examples. Within a week or so during high summer, bindweeds can obscure a rusting tangle of barbed wire, a telegraph pole, or a crumbling wall and lend a brief illusion of beauty to the most uncompromising object. The secret of their success lies in a network of creeping underground rootstocks that can regenerate even when chopped into small pieces, and in the plants' rapid ability to produce rampant flowering stems.

Because they share with the bindweeds a similar tolerance of pollutants, creeping underground stems or vigorous tap roots, and copious seed production, the Compositae make up quite a large proportion of urban perennials. The more common members include daisies (*Bellis*), ox eye daisies (*Chrysanthemum*), golden rod (*Solidago*), chamomiles (*Anthemis*), dandelions (*Taraxacum*), yarrow (*Achillea*) and tansy (*Tanacetum*).

One of the most dramatically successful of urban weeds in northern Europe, however, is the rosebay willowherb (*Epilobium angustifolium*). Most willowherbs possess annual flowering stems with tough perennial creeping rootstocks by which they spread prolifically in a local area. An opportunist, rosebay was offered a bonanza of sites during the last war, when many cities were ripped open by bombing, exposing fertile soil that might not have seen the light of day for centuries.

The seeds are efficiently airborne on their feathery extensions, and are able to germinate rapidly once they find suitable conditions. As a result rosebay spread far and wide and is now among the commonest of urban wild flowers, making a brilliant splash of colour as it takes over waste ground. It is also particularly suited to burnt ground and, like the Oxford ragwort, has taken advantage of man's activities. In the age of steam trains, when hot coals often set light to embankments, *E. angustifolium* rapidly colonized the areas neighbouring railway lines.

Left A number of species of bindweed, including the small bindweed (*Convolvulus arvensis*), will clothe large areas of waste ground, spreading their weak stems by vigorous and deeply penetrating rootstocks.

Above Tansy (*Tanacetum vulgare*) is adapted to cope with urban life. It has deep tough roots, is resistant to pollutants, and produces large numbers of seeds from its compact yellow "button" flower heads.

Defensive measures

Stinging nettles (*Urtica*) are the most ubiquitous of perennial urban weeds, having developed a particular brand of above-ground defence that renders them invulnerable to all but the most dedicated of assault. When the stinging hairs are touched, the sharp tips puncture the skin and break, and the irritants contained in the hairs are squirted out under pressure.

Below the soil, the plant spreads by a tough tangle of rootstocks, but nettles have also been equipped in other less obvious ways. The flowers are small and wind pollinated, and to help the process each stamen is at first folded inwards so that when ripe, it will spring up violently, discharging a cloud of pollen grains.

Other opportunist perennials include the thistles (*Carduus*), which are also equipped with special defences of spines and deep, penetrating rootstocks, that can survive the most rigorous of assaults. Thistles also produce large numbers of airborne seeds. Similarly, the docks (*Rumex*) develop massive, branching tap roots that penetrate far below a single spade-depth, and the flowering spikes generate large numbers of tiny wind-blown seeds.

The commonest shrub of urban waste ground is the butterfly bush (*Buddleia*) which we will look at more closely in the next chapter. Elder (*Sambucus*) and lilac (*Syringa*) also regularly make appearances, either as genuinely wild forms, or as naturalized escapes from gardens. All are major links in the web of urban wildlife, since they produce heavily-scented insect-luring flowers with abundant nectar.

Above The common stinging nettle (*Urtica dioica*) possesses distinctive defensive armaments. Its stinging hairs penetrate the skin and break, releasing a chemical irritant.

Below One of the earliest of the Compositae to flower on urban waste ground is coltsfoot (*Tussilago farfara*). The erect flowering stems bloom in spring before the large angular basal leaves appear.

ESCAPES

Many of the so-called weeds that appear in the urban landscape are either exotic escapes from gardens or accidental imports. The Californian poppy (*Eschscholzia californica*) is a North American weed introduced into European gardens for its glorious flowers; like all poppies, however, it is an opportunist, and has spread beyond the garden fence wherever the European climate is mild enough.

The biennial honesty (*Lunaria*) is likewise cultivated for its showy blooms and silvery ornamental siliculas, as are the garden lupins (*Lupinus*), which were introduced originally from North America as colourful herbaceous border plants. Both readily escape and establish themselves on urban waste ground.

Many of the cultivated umbellifers have become naturalized and grow side by side with more local invasive weeds, such as hogweed (*Heracleum sphondylium*). Fennel (*Foeniculum vulgare*), easily recognizable with its feathery aromatic foliage and yellow flower heads, probably originates from southern Europe, but is now established all over Europe, particularly in dry situations near the sea. Coriander (*Coriandrum*) is an annual, native to the Levant, but it too has spread as a weed of cultivation, as have such garden pests as ground elder or goutweed (*Aegopodium podagraria*). Native to damp woodlands, this last was originally cultivated for its value as a medicinal plant.

Edible plants

Historical associations provide much of the interest when discovering urban botany. One of the most beautiful flowers of inner city wasteland is the summer annual known as evening primrose (*Oenothera*). Related to the willowherbs, this bears showy spikes of papery yellow flowers which open in early morning, close in the heat of the day, and re-open in early evening. *Oenothera* originates in north America, but as many as eight different species were brought to Europe, most of them early in the 17th century, to be cultivated,

Above California poppies (*Eschscholzia*) were introduced from North America. Used to hotter climates and poor sandy soils, the leaves are finely cut to reduce their transpiration area, and the flowers close in cool or dull weather.

Left Another plant indigenous to North America, the lupin (*Lupinus*), is a member of the pea family. Cultivated by gardeners for its lovely blooms, escapes are now found all over urban wasteland.

partly for their blooms, but also for the edible roots. Tasting not unlike parsnip these have, at times, rivalled the potato in popularity.

The tiny, creeping silverweed (*Potentilla anserina*), a low-growing rosette plant which can tolerate a high degree of exposure, occurs in stony pastures and waste ground throughout Europe, but much of its dispersal in northern latitudes is due to its having been grown as a fodder crop. A member of the rose family, silverweed bears pretty yellow flowers but was cultivated for its

Above Other than accidental imports, most exotic escapes, such as honesty (*Lunaria*), possess features that make them popular with gardeners. The pretty purple racemes of honesty ripen to the familiar flat silvery silicula fruits used for indoor decorations.

Right Some imported escapes have enjoyed practical uses: a number of evening primrose (*Oenothera*) species have been introduced and grown, not only for their large papery yellow flowers, but on occasions as root vegetables.

highly nutritious roots. These have at times staved off famine, particularly in remote island communities, like those in the British Shetlands, which experience long periods of adverse weather.

A sizable number of the plants which, today, we might class as worthless weeds were grown in kitchen gardens two hundred years ago, and remain as pointers to our forgotten feeding habits. Nettles, chamomiles, sorrels and mugworts were all an essential part of the 18th century housewife's repertoire, and many other plants of towns and cities possess common names that provide clues to their past value. Related to fat hen (*Chenopodium album*) is good King Henry (*C. bonus-Henricus*). Its shoots develop each year from a perennial rootstock, and the leaves are not unlike spinach in appearance and taste.

The plant favours richly-manured ground, and therefore it often grows where there are farm dung heaps. Various traditions suggest that its name is attributable to English, French and German monarchs.

137

it escaped on to waste ground, where it thrived on open middens and rubbish heaps. Nowadays, with the coming of urban sanitation and more scientific dental care, henbane has become a comparative rarity, but it still appears close to the sites of old villages, monasteries and castles.

Tobacco (*Nicotiana tabacum*) is an exotic species which has been introduced and spread widely through the milder climates of Europe. It was grown principally as an ornamental, because of its pale showy blooms, but it also synthesizes dangerous poisons which, in controlled amounts, have been used medicinally.

Left By popular tradition, Alexander's pot herb (*Smyrnium olusatrum*) was distributed through the military advances of Alexander the Great. It is one of the few umbellifers with large leaves and yellow flowers.

Below The oraches, such as *Atriplex patula*, have been cultivated as spinach-like vegetables. Covered in a fine greyish "meal", this species is one of the commonest. The flowers are unusual – small and knobbly, in greyish spikes.

Amongst the umbellifers with descriptive names, Alexander's pot herb (*Smyrnium olusatrum*) is indigenous to much of Europe, but has been cultivated as a vegetable, according to popular traditions, since the time of Alexander the Great. It is one of the few yellow-flowered members of the parsley group to bear large entire or partly-cut leaves, and it is generally found growing on chalky soil near the sea.

Medicinal herbs

Many plants were grown in urban areas, not primarily as food plants, but as medicinal herbs. This is particularly true of several members of the Solanaceae family, including henbane (*Hyoscyamus niger*), which is an unpleasant-smelling coarsely-hairy annual, with yellowish trumpet-shaped flowers and distinctive seed capsules. It is essentially a Mediterranean plant, but during the Middle Ages it was spread prolifically almost anywhere that there was human habitation. The reason for this was that it was grown as a herbal remedy for toothache, thanks to its narcotic properties. In time,

Above Past utilitarian value is often a clue to explain the presence of wild plants in urban areas. Soapwort (*Saponaria officinalis*), when rubbed, produces a soapy substance.

The most notorious of the Solanaceae is deadly nightshade (*Atropa belladonna*), a plant of Mediterranean origin. Annual stems arise in a typically arching fashion from a perennial rootstock, and bear dull purplish flowers with the trumpet-shape characteristic of the family. The fruit is a distinctive glossy berry, violet or black in colour and lozenge-like in shape, which is intensely poisonous. In fact, the Latin name of the plant reveals much of its character: *Atropa* derives from the Greek word *atropos* meaning "fate", while *belladonna* means "beautiful lady". One of the side-effects of the poison is to dilate the pupils of the eyes. The seeds were carried in the baggage of the Roman legions and their families, aristocratic ladies used drops of belladonna tincture to make their eyes appear large and mysterious! The plant has been a popular source of poison, as well as a medication, when used in more properly controlled doses. It tends to grow throughout Europe, therefore, round the sites of ancient castles and monasteries, where it has been cultivated and since gone wild.

Both comfrey (*Symphytum*) and mallow (*Malva*) are plants with medicinal properties that have been valued since the time of the Greeks. Comfrey is a

Above Medicinal use has often resulted in the continued presence of wild flowers close to town centres. Mallow (*Malva sylvestris*) was once among the most valued of medicinal herbs, being used to treat a wide range of ailments.

distinctive hairy perennial which has managed to escape into shady waste places everywhere in Europe. Its leaf blades extend down into the branching stems, and the cream or purple flowers droop. Mallow, with its delicate pink and purple blooms, is one of the most beautiful flowers of waste ground. The Mediterranean region supports tall tree mallows (*M. mauritiana*), but dwarf and common mallows (*M. rotundifolia* and *M. sylvestris*) are found extensively across all but extreme northern latitudes of Europe.

SOIL AND POLLUTANTS

It is important to remember, when looking at an urban habitat, that the soil type may be peculiar, not merely to the location, but even to a small patch of that area. The soil can be affected in many ways. Chalk may have been dumped on a neutral clay soil as a foundation hard core.

The site may have been utilized in past times as an ash heap. It may also include disproportionately high levels of nitrates from domestic effluent. All these things can have a positive or negative effect on the plants growing in the immediate area. Furthermore, air-borne pollutants can have a considerable influence on what will or will not grow.

Lichens

Lichens are extremely sensitive to air pollution and are therefore very accurate pollution indicators in the urban environment. A fascinating study for the botanist is to examine the incidence of key lichen species in relation to traffic fumes and industrial sites. These primitive living associations between an alga and a fungus obtain their nutrient salts by absorbing them from air and rainwater. Thus, atmospheric pollutants accumulate in the plants, with detrimental results. Prior to the clean-up of smoke emissions in large European cities, most lichens had disappeared from inner urban areas, and the range growing in suburbs was restricted to only the most robust species.

As controls have been introduced, however, through clean-air legislation in various countries, even the rarer lichen species have begun to increase in urban areas. A good illustration is the lichen *Evernia prunastri*. Until the mid-1980s this very sensitive species could be found no nearer to the centre of London than the outer suburbs, where it occurred only very sporadically. Now, the species has managed to establish itself in the heart of the city, in parts of Green and Hyde Parks.

Lichens are divided into a number of types. *Fructicose* lichens, of which *Evernia* is one, are bushy, either standing erect or hanging down from a single stalk at the base. Others include the *Ramalina* and *Usnea* species. *Foliose* lichens include common members of the *Parmelia* family, in which the thallus tends to creep horizontally and is attached by small threads. A third type are described as *crustose* lichens, and these as

Testing soil samples

The first assessment of any soil must be to check its components. All soils are made up of particles of rock that have been broken down and pulverized by the action of glacial ice, wind, water, and earth movements such as landslides. Even if it is totally pure clay or sand, a soil will be made up of a combination of particles of differing sizes, and virtually all soils contain a proportion of organic humus. Typically, if you cut a vertical section through a soil you will find three zones: an upper layer of topsoil which is dark and rich in humus, a lighter subsoil, and finally the bedrock which largely influences the soil's nature.

To identify a soil type, put soil into a jam jar, having removed the large stones. When the jar is a quarter full of soil, add water to the three-quarter level, fit the lid and shake thoroughly. Leave the jar to stand. After about an hour you will notice several distinct layers: floating at the surface will be organic debris; the finer clay particles will be in the upper layers, and the heavier sand and gravel particles will be at the bottom. The proportions will offer a good measure of the soil consistency.

To test the acidity or alkalinity – the pH – of the soil, various inexpensive kits are available from hardware shops and garden centres. Neutral pH is 7. If the pH value is lower – for example, pH 6 – the soil will be acid; if it is higher it will be alkaline. The simplest kit uses indicator papers. The soil is wetted; the paper strip inserted, and the resulting colour change should be compared with a standard chart.

A more accurate method uses indicator liquid(s). A small sample of soil is placed in the test tube that is provided with the kit, and the solution is added and shaken. Once, again, the resulting colour should be matched against a standard chart.

Above Lichens provide one of the most accurate biological indicators of atmospheric pollution. Primitive associations of algae and fungi, each plant absorbs its nutrient salts directly from moisture in the air or from rain water. With clean air acts affecting many European cities, lichens are gradually making a return to such habitats.

the name suggests, spread as a crust. The most ubiquitous is the yellow lichen *Xanthoria parietina* which frequently appears on buildings.

It is interesting to look for the reproductive structures of lichens. They are spread by spores borne in microscopic sacs called *asci*, which are packed together tightly in a fruiting body. Called an *apothecium* if it is open and saucer-shaped, this becomes a *perithecium* when closed apart from a small pore at the apex. Notice, also, that in the *Parmelia, Ramalina* and *Physcia* species, warty masses may appear on the thallus. These are known as *soralia* and contain minute vegetative fragments or *soredia*, which are blown about in the air currents, settling under suitable conditions to form new lichens.

Lichens have little economic importance, though the *Cladonia* group includes reindeer moss, which is vital to animals browsing on frozen tundras. Interestingly, because of the ready ability of lichens to absorb impurities, reindeer moss took on massive radioactivity after the notorious Chernobyl nuclear accident, and this was passed on to northern European reindeer herds, with catastrophic results.

Litmus, the familiar laboratory indicator used to test for acidity and alkalinity, is obtained from lichens as, in the past, were a number of fabric dyes. Lichens also synthesize substances known to have excellent antibiotic qualities.

WILD GARDENING AT HOME
INTRODUCTION

Gardeners and farmers alike will attempt to rid their land of weeds. But why? What constitutes a weed? The bindweed family (Convolvulaceae) offers a sharp illustration – it includes the perfect white bells of the large bindweed (*C. sepium*) on the one hand, and on the other the equally attractive blooms of morning glory (*Ipomoea*), introduced from America. One is regarded as an uninvited pest; the other is encouraged.

The arbitrary decisions that we make, choosing to protect some plants and eliminate others, are important, because now that species of wild flower are disappearing from the countryside at an ever-increasing rate under the onslaught of agriculture and urbanization, our gardens represent important potential refuges. Historically, gardens first came into being as fenced-off areas in which to grow vegetables and other herbs, safe from the ravages of sheep, cattle, horses and pigs. Monastic gardens were developed as repositories of medicinal plants, and as the first places for botanical study. It was only in later ages that gardens became places of beauty and leisure.

A limitation of gardens, from the point of view of the practical botanist, is that they are generally as far removed from constituting a truly wild piece of countryside as is a forest plantation or a cornfield. A garden is designed more for aesthetic appearance and as a leisure facility, than as an authentically natural habitat, and gardens possess an order and control of their population that is not found elsewhere in nature.

It is, however, quite possible for the practical botanist to develop a wild garden at home and to gain a great deal of pleasure from it, even if the available space is limited to a small pocket-handkerchief plot or a window box!

There is a new enthusiasm for wild gardening, and the strict distinction that once existed between weeds and flowers is eroding away. Some of the raw material will probably already be growing in the garden: rockeries are populated, by and large, by plants that are little altered from those growing in alpine regions, and

Below left What constitutes a "weed" or a "flower"? It is all a matter of personal preference. The large bindweed (*Convolvulus sepium*) bears some of the most beautiful of white flowers, yet convention casts it as a garden pest.

Below The seed of wild flowers, including foxglove (*Digitalis purpurea*), can be purchased commercially. Many seedsmen now offer selections to suit a particular soil type or climate, or to reproduce a specific habitat, such as a flower meadow.

herbaceous borders may already be stocked involuntarily with spurges (*Euphorbia*), thistles (*Carduus*), chickweed (*Stellaria*) and nettles (*Urtica*), and, more deliberately, with such attractive flowering plants as himalayan balsam (*Impatiens glandulifera*), violet (*Viola*) and primrose (*Primula*). In the hedge you may find dog rose (*Rosa canina*) and wild clematis (*Clematis vitalba*).

Legal restrictions

Much, though, will have to be obtained from elsewhere. By the early 1980s, many commercial seedsmen had recognized that there was a burgeoning market for wild flowers, and they now offer both potted seedlings, and assortments of wild flower seeds which you can purchase in packets. This is probably the easiest and safest way to obtain raw material. When collected from the wild, there is the problem of obtaining seeds in the right condition, and should you choose to pick your own, beware of national and local rules! In Britain, the Wildlife and Countryside Act prohibits tampering in

Above The landscape designers of the 18th and 19th centuries added a new dimension to gardening, developing the vegetable plots and the formal layouts of the Tudors and Stuarts into the landscaped, but wholly artificial, parklands that grace the countryside today.

any way with a proscribed list of rare wild plants; the ban includes the removal of seeds and cuttings, and there are stiff penalties for offenders.

Other conservation-minded countries now exercise similar restrictions. In Britain, technically speaking, you must also obtain permission from a landowner before you dig up any plant from a moss to a tree (the only exceptions are fungi) even if allowed to do so by law. In any case, if you uproot or pick cuttings of a plant, the risk then exists that they will not survive, having suffered the shock of transport home in the car or on the bus.

If a plant is growing on your own land, it is effectively yours to do with as you please, though you are still liable in principle should it be a rarity.

143

CREATING A WILD GARDEN

So you have decided to start a wild garden. The first thing to do is to assess the habitat which you possess. It may well have a great deal to offer – a European garden can contain up to 100 species of so-called weed, and one of the unnatural advantages of gardens is that characteristically they offer a range of habitats and even climatic conditions. It is a useful exercise to work out how many soil types your own particular garden includes. You may have a basic soil type which is either acid or alkaline, and may be clay, sand or chalk, but within the garden there may be special areas: a raised peat bed, a rockery, walls and other hedges, an area of drained gravel, or a cinder path. In a larger plot, you may also enjoy a wooded area or a stream. All these features can be of potential advantage in creating a wild garden, because all constitute differing habitats.

You will have to make an early decision as to how much of your available space is to be taken up by wilderness, and then you must settle in your mind the extent to which you are prepared to allow it to intrude into your more conventional plot. Are you to have several small areas of wilderness with contrasting features, or a single patch which includes as many aspects as possible? Consider your options on the basis of how much sun the area receives, the soil drainage, possible effect of trees, and exposure.

One of the first considerations should be the direction of the prevailing wind. If your garden is on the windward side, and it includes species of *Rumex*, *Carduus*, *Taraxacum*, or *Epilobium* to name the more notorious examples, you will very soon be enjoying the benefit of these plants everywhere! Your wild garden should therefore, be sited downwind. However, it is equally important that the site of such a plot should be safe from wind-blown herbicides. It should not therefore be located adjacent to an arable field.

If the garden is to include grasses and other species with rampant creeping underground stems, it may be worth "planting" a barrier of bricks to a depth of at least two spades. In any event it is worth serious thought about potential consequences before introducing such pernicious and incursive plants as bindweeds (*Convolvulus*) and ground elder (*Aegopodium*).

Planning a wild garden can provide as much fun as landscaping a conventional one. Let the natural conditions dictate the kind of habitat. Once you have made the crucial choices, clear the ground thoroughly of existing occupants. Remember that if you are planting flower types that are vulnerable to being swamped, the potential competition needs to be removed and kept at bay. Establish the pH of the soil, and the soil type. The fertility of the soil is actually of lesser importance to wild flowers than to cultivars, so there is no need to apply fertilizers or mulches, but a heavy clay soil may be improved by working in some peat and sharp sand.

The wild plants you grow will be governed by the type of soil and the degree of drainage and exposure. It is no good mixing seed from a range of contrasting habitats, throwing it on the soil and hoping for the best. It is also important, unless you are buying commercially-prepared mixtures which will already have been selected on a sound basis of balance, to remember the lessons learned about plant associations. Group together those plants that live side by side in nature. If, for example, you are creating a flower meadow, avoid introducing the kind of large, suffocating species which have, in part, been responsible for the demise of such habitats.

If the ground is well drained and has a sunny, south-facing aspect, go for alpines, xerophytes and Mediter-

Below One of the more ubiquitous members of the Labiatae, and one which has invaded back gardens naturally, is the annual white dead nettle (*Lamium album*).

The erect stems grow from a short creeping stock, and the plant flowers throughout the year, making it a pretty addition to a wild garden.

Right Careful consideration needs to be given before the introduction of dandelions (*Taraxacum officinale*). The seeds are blown about in large numbers and, once established in a manicured lawn, are extremely difficult to eliminate because of the deep-seated tap roots.

ranean plants. If it is cool and shady, with damp heavy clay, it may make an ideal water meadow. The choice is largely a matter of commonsense, but a little forethought and planning can save a great deal of frustration and disappointment later on.

Storing seed

The ground is prepared, and you are ready to introduce the plants. Assuming that you grow from seed, here are some useful tips. If you choose to collect your own seed, it is essential to store it only when it is ripe, but it may be better to collect a flowering stem sooner rather than later, and hang it to ripen in suitable conditions.

The alternative is to leave the fruits on the plant, but this is to risk attack from mammals and birds, as well as from mould infection. Some wild plant seeds require a resting period in cold conditions before they will germinate. Seeds of many alpines, for example, benefit from being frozen for several weeks, and may even remain dormant for up to two years. Others, by contrast, will only germinate if sown immediately on ripening.

Most plants that produce seed in temperate climates are geared to a period of dormancy over winter, so seed collected in the autumn can therefore be kept successfully until the following spring. Avoid using polythene bags, or you may seal moisture in with your seeds; a paper envelope is ideal. Write the name of the seed

indelibly, otherwise you can guarantee to have forgotten what it is by the time you come round to sowing. Store your seeds in a cool dry place, well away from foraging rats and mice. Commercially-marketed seed can safely be assumed to be in proper condition for sowing, though instructions need careful reading.

Sowing seed

Generally speaking, small meadow-flower seeds can be sown into ground which has been raked to loosen the surface. With small-sized seeds they can be broadcast by hand in the old traditional style, though they should only be spread very thinly. All that is required after this, is to rake the seed in gently, covering it if possible with a light layer of sharp sand and loam, and then rolling it so as to give a reasonable protection from birds.

If the seed is large, as with *Lupinus*, it should be sown a little deeper, ideally at a depth equal to its own diameter. Seeds such as those of *Epilobium* will have a better chance of germination if sown with the "feather" pointing upwards.

Seed which is broadcast and allowed its chances will produce a natural-looking result, but suffers greater risk of being blown away, eaten by birds or trampled. The alternative is to sow the seed in trays, and then prick out and transplant the seedlings in a reasonably haphazard fashion.

Above Introducing thistles, including the pretty musk thistle (*Carduus nutans*) requires advanced planning. Members of the Compositae, like dandelion, they generate large numbers of airborne seeds and resist attempts at removal.

Right When taking a cutting, use a sharp knife and cut off a shoot below an axillary bud or at a branch, leaving a heel. Remove the lower leaves, dust with rooting hormone powder and place in compost.

Cuttings

Digging up whole plants and transporting them will give you a head start for a season or more, but you will incur the drawbacks already mentioned. Propagation from cuttings is the surest way to guarantee the exact variety that you hope to grow, but in many cases this will not be practical or viable. Most alpines and shrubby plants will, however, propagate successfully from cuttings. Using a sharp blade, detach a small shoot cleanly, either just below an axillary bud or at a branch, so that a heel is left, and then carefully trim off the lowest leaves. The cutting should be dabbed with rooting hormone powder and pushed firmly into a suitable cutting compost.

Above Ground elder (*Aegopodium podagraria*) is a coarse, tenacious perennial, growing from creeping rootstocks. It was cultivated extensively as "goutweed" for medicinal purposes and is now a garden pest. The plant was probably introduced into Britain but is indigenous elsewhere in Europe.

Right The hellebore species (*Helleborus*), related to the buttercups, often produce flowers during the winter and include many garden hybrids. Note how the sepals are retained until the large fruit is almost ripe.

LAWNS AND MEADOWS

It is probably best to resist the temptation to grow wild flowers in a British-style closely-mown lawn unless they are early, spring-flowering bulbs and corms, such as snowdrops, bluebells, wild daffodils, and crocuses. Lawns in some countries are merely roughly-mown fields; in others, they are symbols of affluence, immaculately manicured and sanitized with regular applications of fertilizer and weedkiller! The result is a lush, green desert, in many respects the suburban equal of a cornfield, composed entirely of selected and screened grasses. Obviously, you will be unable to mow your lawn if the introduced species flower in high summer, and in any case the types of grass from which the lawn is built may grow so thickly as to suffocate many of the smaller flowers.

Creating a flower meadow

A flower meadow is best created elsewhere, in a plot where the suitability of the soil and the aspect have been assessed, and the area cleared of any existing weeds. Among the commercially-available seed mixtures, it is now possible in many European countries to buy selected flower-meadow seed. At least one specialist firm in England, Emorsgate Seeds, export world-wide. They will supply a mix appropriate to your soil type, whether it is alluvial, clay or sandy, and they even produce special mixtures for water meadows.

The range of species will vary, but generally a flower-meadow garden will include the more common meadow flowers, such as corn poppies (*Papaver rhoeas*), scented mayweeds (*Anthemis*), field scabious (*Scabiosa*) and rampion (*Phyteuma*), as well as some of the rarities that urgently need protection. Among these will be cornflower (*Centaurea cyanus*), corn cockle *(Agrostemma githago)* and corn marigold (*Chrysanthemum segetum*).

Ideally, once established, such a meadow should be grazed or scythed to keep it under some control, but apart from this it will require little maintenance.

Walls and paths

Other parts of the garden will lend themselves to a display of mosses and liverworts. If you have a pathway of cinder or old gravel, look closely at any shaded areas, perhaps beside a north- or east-facing wall. Among the cinders you may well find the small liverwort *Lunularia* is already growing, easily identified by its crescent-shaped gemmae cups. The same path may support other liverworts, such as *Marchantia*, or where the ground is slightly less damp and gloomy, a range of mosses, including fire mosses *Funaria* and

Left Mosses, including the common wall moss *Tortula muralis*, can soften the appearance of a wall. They also provide a fascinating botanical study. Look for the tiny male and female "flowers" in early spring; these are followed by the capsules of spores.

Far left Greater periwinkle (*Vinca major*) is a common undershrub in shady places in and near gardens. The typically solitary blue flowers make a good subject for drawing. Notice how the corolla tube divides into five broad segments.

Left On chalk downlands look out for the round-headed rampion (*Phyteuma orbiculare*). Growing from a short thick rootstock, the simple stems carry the flower heads upwards to compete with the surrounding grasses.

Centre Toadflax (*Linaria*) is one of the prettiest small yellow flowers of grassland. It is a good example of a zygomorphic flower in which the spur of the corolla tube is long and pointed.

Below Pennywort (*Cotyledon umbilicus*) grows well in sunny positions on dry walls. Arising from woody root stock, the distinctively-shaped leaves are fleshy and crenate, and the flowers, borne on longer stalks, are greenish yellow.

Leptobryum, and *Ceratodon*. You may also find seedlings of flowering plants such as rosebay (*Epilobium angustifolium*). On a sunny wall beside the path, there may be the delicate *Tortula muralis*, or one of the *Bryum* species – a group of mosses particularly able to withstand a polluted atmosphere. Modern brick walls with hard mortar in the joints are not ideal places for many wall plants, but if the material is old and crumbly, you may find ferns such as wall rue (*Asplenium ruta-muraria*), and a range of typical flowering plants, such as pennywort (*Cotyledon umbilicus*). Others can be introduced quite easily, as long as you provide them with a small pocket of earth and some generous watering until their roots have penetrated.

PHYSIC GARDENS

Physic gardens provide their own fascination. The idea may have originated in Italy, where the first garden designed specifically to grow and dispense medicinal plants was probably established at Pisa in 1543. Similar gardens followed at Florence and Padua, and these were associated with the great centres of learning and science. It was an age when exploration of far-flung regions of the world was gaining momentum, and many exotic genera and species were being brought back to Europe by travellers. The famous 16th-century botanist, Charles de l'Ecluse, set up a physic garden in

Left Among the most gracious of potherbs that can be introduced into a wild garden, fennel (*Foeniculum vulgare*) grows as a tall umbellifer with long feathery-cut leaves and yellow flower heads. The whole plant is edible and delicately aromatic.

Above The opium poppy (*Papaver somniferum*) has been hybridized extensively, and cultivars now frequently grow on waste ground. The colour of the flowers varies considerably and they often appear as double heads.

Vienna at the command of Emperor Maximilian II in 1573, and a hundred years later the famous Chelsea Physic Garden was established in London by the Worshipful Society of Apothecaries.

Many of these gardens combined medicinal and culinary purposes, as did tens of thousands of cottage gardens all over Europe, but on a grander and more scientific scale. It is difficult to establish whether food or medicine actually came first; normally, the two probably went hand in hand.

Medicinal species

Among the more important species cultivated were many which are now generally considered as urban weeds – thorn apple (*Datura stramonium*), valerian (*Valeriana officinalis*), comfrey (*Symphytum offic-

Right Some plants have enjoyed popular medicinal use for less than scientific reasons. St John's Wort (*Hypericum perforatum*) possesses astringent properties, but its main claim to fame is the bright red oil glands in its leaves, which gave it a reputation for treating wounds.

inale), tansy (*Chrysanthemum vulgare*) and the opium poppy (*Papaver somniferum*). Some had genuine medicinal properties; others were introduced on a less scientific evaluation. Although it undoubtedly has soothing and astringent properties, St John's wort (*Hypericum perforatum*) was first noticed because its leaves, which have small perforations, also display bright red oil glands. On the homoeopathic principle of like curing like, an extract of the wort was used in treating wounds, ulcers and burns.

Other popular wild introductions to gardens of bygone eras included such species as angelica (*Angelica archangelica*), rosemary (*Rosmarinus officinalis*), rue (*Ruta graveolens*), mugwort (*Artemisia vulgaris*) and parsley (*Petroselinum crispum*). Names are sometimes a give-away clue to the old usage – the

potentillas, among them cinquefoil (*P. reptans*), obtained their name as a derivative of the word "potent", and cinquefoil was once valued as a sedative and for its use in the treatment of epilepsy.

Growing herbs

Most herbs are of Mediterranean origin, and if you decide to cultivate a herb garden you must plant your herbs in a well-drained alkaline soil, which benefits from plenty of sun. Traditionally, the Elizabethan gardeners of England planted herbs in knot gardens – geometric designs planted with herbs of contrasting colours and textures. One of the simplest modern variations is to lay out an area with bricks or paving slabs, interspersed with small beds, so that all the plants are easily accessible.

PONDS

An indispensable area of a wild garden should be a pond. It does not have to be very big, but if it is to be effective as a piece of wilderness, it needs to be designed in the right way.

The siting of the pond is all-important. If you place it too near a house, mosquitos can become a serious nuisance. Overhanging trees can also be a problem, making the water stagnant by depleting the pond of light, and shedding their leaves during the autumn so that they accumulate at the bottom.

The key design factors are the depth, the nature of the bottom, and the perimeter. If you live in a part of temperate Europe that is subject to prolonged sub-zero temperatures, the pond must be deep enough to prevent it from freezing down to the bottom, which will kill off plant and animal inhabitants alike. To survive an average mild winter, the pond will need to be at least 60cm deep in some parts, but where there is a likelihood of more severe and prolonged frosts, an additional 30cm of water depth is advisable.

Conversely, if you live in a Mediterranean climate, the chief necessity will be to aerate the water in order to prevent oxygen starvation, and it will be essential to have an electrically driven pump to create an adequate water flow.

It is immaterial whether the pond is created out of a pre-formed plastic liner, a polythene sheet or concrete, but there should be a layer of sand and loam on the bottom. A squeaky-clean pond is not a proper pond! One end of the water garden needs to be inclined gently up into shallows no more than 20cm deep. This incline has several important functions: it creates an area of swamp and marsh in which marginals can be grown; it provides shelter, and it also permits aquatic and amphibian animals to enter and leave the deeper areas safely. If the pond area can be combined with flowing water in a stream, so much the better, with the reservation that the rate of flow should be sluggish, as many aquatic plants dislike life in strongly running water.

Left Water mint (Mentha aquatica) is a good hardy perennial to introduce round the margins of a pond. In the wild, it grows in wet ditches and marshes and along the edges of streams. The flowers are a delicate bluish mauve.

Above right The design of a garden pond is all-important if a major consideration is to encourage wildlife. Access in and out of the pond and a careful balance of plants to provide fresh clear water are among the factors to take into account.

Below right Myosotis scorpioides, the water forget-me-not, can be found in ditches and along stream sides throughout Europe. Growing from a perennial rootstock, the weak straggling stems bear clear blue flowers. The common forget-me-not is a distinct species.

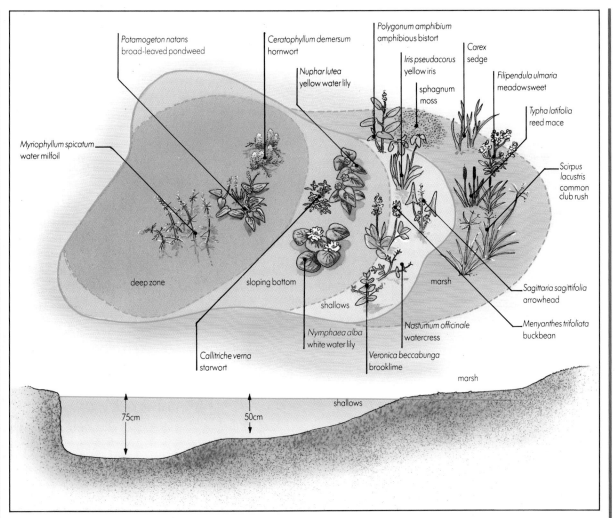

Potamogeton natans
broad-leaved pondweed

Ceratophyllum demersum
hornwort

Nuphar lutea
yellow water lily

Polygonum amphibium
amphibious bistort

Iris pseudacorus
yellow iris

sphagnum
moss

Carex
sedge

Filipendula ulmaria
meadowsweet

Typha latifolia
reed mace

Myriophyllum spicatum
water milfoil

Scirpus
lacustris
common
club rush

deep zone

sloping bottom

shallows

marsh

Sagittaria sagittifolia
arrowhead

Callitriche verna
starwort

Nymphaea alba
white water lily

Nasturtium officinale
watercress

Menyanthes trifoliata
buckbean

Veronica beccabunga
brooklime

marsh

shallows

75cm

50cm

Choosing pond plants

The choice of plants is yours, but with a word or two of warning. It is not advisable to introduce Canadian pond weed (*Elodea canadensis*) because of its rampant spread and the peculiar stagnant conditions that it generates. Duckweed (*Lemna*) and the floating fern *Azolla* should be avoided at all costs, because of their adverse habit of totally screening the water, and if water lilies are to be planted, make sure that the pads obscure only a limited area of the water from sunlight. Algal growth should be removed as far as possible with a rake or net, since it encourages stagnancy and blocks out light. The best cure for algae, though, is prevention. Algae will only thrive if there is an abundant supply of nitrate in the water. If there are enough aquatic flowering plants competing for the available minerals, algal bloom will be effectively suppressed. It is all a matter of achieving the correct balance.

153

ENCOURAGING INSECTS

It is impossible to be a botanist without noticing that plants are part of a web of life that includes mammals, birds, insects, snails, slugs and beetles. For many animals, the plants are an indispensible source of shelter, food and raw materials. By a similar token, plants need animals for pollination, seed dispersal, and occasionally to supplement their nutrition

It is worth luring pollinating insects into a garden, and several plants represent outstanding attractants. The buddleia (*B. davidii*) is known, not without justification, as the butterfly bush. To see the dense spikes

Left Ivy (*Hedera helix*) bears dense umbels of rather undistinguished yellow-green flowers in late autumn, when few other species are in bloom. It provides an important source of nectar for foraging bees.

Above Some plants are valuable because they provide signals that attract insects at specific times of the day. The honeysuckle (*Lonicera periclymenum*) gives out a potent fragrance in the evening.

of mauve flowers on this deciduous shrub smothered in feeding butterflies in high summer is a delight. Amongst the sedums, *S. spectabile*, with its splendid heads of deep pink flowers in later summer, is another certain lure for bees, hoverflies and butterflies. In late autumn, ivy (*Hedera*) will also attract bees to forage on one of the few nectars available after summer flowers have finished.

More specifically, plants like rosebay (*Epilobium angustifolium*) will encourage the caterpillars of the elephant hawk moth; nettles (*Urtica*) attract those of peacock and red admiral butterflies. Many flowers, including those of red poppy (*P. rhoeas*) and evening primrose (*Oenothera*), display particular features in the ultra-violet end of the light spectrum. These markings are visible to insects, though not to us, and they serve as guide tracks to lure bees and moths towards the nectaries. Other plants, such as honeysuckle (*Lonicera pericyclamen*), exude a particularly strong perfume in the evening, designed to attract those insects which fly in the twilight hours.

One unexpected bonus, amongst the many which come from a wild garden, is that unwelcome insects are often reduced substantially. A good variety of weeds will encourage such predators as ladybirds and other beetles, and these are a major scourge of less popular invaders including aphids.

Below Columbine (*Aquilegia vulgare*) offers a distinctive flower for the botanical artist. Each petal possesses a long spur which hangs below the calyx.

Right The star of the veldt (*Dimorphotheca pluvialis*) provides an excellent demonstration, among popular garden plants, of movement in response to sunlight. The flowers remain closed on dull days and will also close when placed in the shade

GLOSSARY

abscission: rupturing of leaf stalk base in autumn.

achene: non-fleshy single-seeded fruit.

actinomorphic: descriptive of radially symmetrical flower.

adventitious root: root developing in unusual part of a plant e.g. along a stem.

aerenchyma: type of flotation tissue in aquatic plants.

algae: very simple green plants generally living in water.

angiosperms: highest class of flowering plants.

annual: plant reaching maturity and completing life cycle in a single season.

anther: organ of flower generating male cells or pollen.

antheridia: reproductive organs containing motile male cells, seen in primitive plants.

antipetaly: condition in which stamens are arranged opposite to petals.

archegonia: reproductive organs containing female cells, seen in primitive plants.

axillary bud: bud in the angle made between a stem and a leaf.

berry: type of fruit.

biennial: plant developing vegetatively in first year and flowering and fruiting in second.

bract: highly specialized leaf usually with protective function.

bulb: modified shoot used for vegetative propagation, consisting of shortened stem and fleshy scale leaves.

calyx: outermost part of a flower usually consisting of green leaf-like sepals.

cambium: area of permanently young cells responsible for lateral (girth) growth in a stem.

capitulum: type of inflorescence.

carpel: female reproductive organ of a flowering plant.

chloroplast: microscopic structure within cell, containing chlorophyll, and concerned with photosynthesis.

cilia: fine hairs.

composite flower: inflorescence made up of many small florets.

coppicing: pruning of a stump to ground level to encourage production of numerous branches.

corm: swollen stem base containing food, used for vegetative propagation.

corolla: conspicuous coloured part of the flower within the calyx.

cotyledon: fleshy seed leaf nourishing the embryo.

corymb: type of inflorescence.

cryptogam: non-flowering plant.

cupule: sheath of bracts protecting a fruit.

cuticle: impervious waxy coating to an epidermis.

dioecious: condition in which unisexual flowers arise on separate plants.

drupe: type of fleshy fruit.

dystrophic: condition of fresh water lakes.

embryo: young plant contained in the seed.

epidermis: outer layer of cells.

epigynous: condition in which the other flower parts are arranged on the gynoecium.

epiphyte: plant attached to another plant but using it only for support.

eutrophic: condition of fresh water lakes.

fertilization: union of male cells from pollen grain with female ovum.

filament: stalk surmounted by anther.

floret: single-petalled and sessile flower.

fruit: the result of fertilization of a flower.

fungi: a class of simple plants, usually parasitic or saprophytic, and containing no chlorophyll.

gamete: reproductive cell.

gametophyte: plant generation producing gametes.

gemmae: special areas of vegetative reproduction seen in some liverworts.

geotropism: plant movement in response to gravity.

girdle scar: position of last year's terminal bud.

glabrous: hairless.

glaucous: with bluish tinge.

glumes: parts of grass inflorescence.

gynoecium: collective term for flower carpels.

halophyte: plant adapted for life in a salt marsh.

herb: plant with parts which do not persist for more than one season above ground.

herbaceous: plant having character of a herb.

herbarium: repository of dried or preserved botanical material.

heterophylly: more than one type of leaf on the same plant.

hydrophyte: aquatic plant.

hypha: thread-like structure of fungal tissue.

hypogynous: condition in which gynoecium is at the apex of other flower parts.

inflorescence: flowering shoot made up of flowers.

internode: length of stem between nodes.

involucre: whorl of bracts.

lichen: primitive association of alga and fungus.

lignin: strengthening material laid down in the tissues of woody plants.

liverwort: primitive plant dependent on damp shady conditions.

locule: cavity within an ovary made up of fused carpels.

meristem: area of permanently youthful tissue responsible for growth of an organ.

metabolism: the chemical processes occurring within a living organism.

monoecious: condition in which male and female flowers are borne separately on the same plant.

mosses (musci): a class of simple green plants.

mycelium: collection of fungal hyphae.

mycorrhiza: improperly understood relationship between certain species of fungi and tree roots.

node: position on stem where leaf or axillary bud arises.

nut: type of dry fruit with woody ovary wall.

oligotrophic: condition of fresh water lakes.

osmosis: process by which a weak solution is carried through a membrane to a stronger one.

panicle: type of inflorescence.

pappus: fan of hairs used in dispersal of a fruit.

parasite: organism gaining the whole of its life requirements from another living organism.

pedicel: stalk of individual flower.

peduncle: stalk of inflorescence.

perennial: plant with rootstock from which it continues growth year by year.

perianth: whorl of petals and sepals.

petal: one of the parts of the flower corolla.

perigynous: condition in which gynoecium is surrounded by other flower parts.

petiole: stalk bearing a leaf.

phloem: food-transporting system within the plant.

photosynthesis: process by which green plants use energy of sunlight to convert simple inorganic compounds into food.

phototropism: plant movement in response to light.

pistil: the gynoecium of a flower.

pollarding: pruning of a trunk above ground level to produce an abundance of branches.

pollination: transfer of pollen from anther to stigma.

pome: type of fleshy fruit.

receptacle: apex of flower stalk bearing floral parts.

rhizome: underground stem serving for vegetative propagation.

rosette: flat whorl of leaves close to the ground.

runner: horizontal stem rooting at the tip and forming a new plant by vegetative propagation.

samara: type of dry winged fruit.

saprophyte: organism gaining its nutrients from dead or dying organic matter.

sepal: one of the parts forming the calyx of a dicotyledonous flower.

sessile: organ without stalk.

shrub: woody perennial plant generally lacking a main trunk.

silicula: type of dry fruit (pod).

siliqua: type of dry fruit (pod).

spike: type of inflorescence.

sporangium: organ producing spores.

sporophyte: plant generation producing spores.

stamen: pollen-producing organ of the flower.

stigma: receptive tip of pistil.

stomata: transpiration pores typically found on a leaf surface.

style: hollow column connecting style and ovary.

sucker: aerial stem arising from a root distant from the main stem.

symbiosis: association of one plant with another dissimilar plant to their mutual advantage.

terminal bud: dormant bud at apex of stem.

thallus: barely differentiated plate-like structure of primitive plants.

torus: flattened receptacle of a flower.

transpiration: evaporation of water from leaf surface.

tree: woody perennial plant with main trunk and branches often reaching massive size.

tuber: swollen tip of underground stem containing stored food and serving for vegetative propagation.

turion: overwintering bud in aquatic plants.

umbel: type of inflorescence.

xerophyte: plant adapted to life in arid conditions.

xylem: water transporting system within the plant.

zygomorphic: descriptive of bilaterally symmetrical flower.

INDEX

Page numbers in **bold** refer to illustrations

Acknowledgements
p27 The Linnean Society Library, London
p37 Sylvia Pepper